Faraday
AS A DISCOVERER

Faraday
AS A DISCOVERER

BY JOHN TYNDALL
Superintendent of the Royal Institution
(1867–1887)

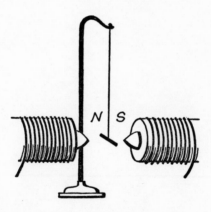

Introduction and notes by KEITH GORDON IRWIN
Illustrated with diagrams

THOMAS Y. CROWELL COMPANY · NEW YORK

Introduction
by Keith Gordon Irwin

*Professor Emeritus in the College of Science and Arts,
Colorado State University*

THE HISTORICAL SETTING

IN THE summer of 1858, Michael Faraday reached retirement age. He was a man of sixty-seven. For thirty-eight years he had been in charge of the famous research laboratory of the Royal Institution on Albemarle Street in London. During that time he had made enormous contributions to the science of physics and chemistry. In particular, he had been the pioneer in developing the facts, relations, principles, and laws of the electric current. Upon his findings would be built,

v

in the coming decades, such practical electrical devices as the telegraph, telephone, motor, generator and transformer, and the use of electricity in silver plating. His use of the words *electrode, anode, cathode,* and *ion* would soon be common ones for even the beginning student in electricity.

He died in September 1867, in the pretty cottage home at Hampton Court Green, to the west of London along the Thames River, which he and his wife had occupied after his retirement.

Four months later, John Tyndall, professor of physics at the Institution, gave a memorial discourse on "Faraday as Scientist and Man." Delivered before a capacity audience at the large lecture hall of the Institution on January 17 and 24, 1868, the discourse was not intended as a eulogy or a life of Faraday, as these terms are usually used. It was, instead, a thoughtful appraisal of the scientific work of this man who had been a great pioneering discoverer. The audience he was addressing was composed of young people as well as old. Some in the listening group had known Faraday in a personal way. As scientists some were aware of the main contributions made by the great discoverer. But there were others, either too young or not proficient in science, who wanted to hear about the work of this great Englishman. For that diversified audience the speaker had a message. Primarily he was speaking of the work of Faraday the scientist, but he wove into that story something about Faraday the man.

The result was a masterful discourse, informing and interesting. He concluded his summary with the ringing words, "Taking him for all in all, I think it will be conceded that Michael Faraday was the greatest experimental philosopher that the world has ever seen; and I will add the opinion that the progress of future research will tend not to dim or diminish, but to enhance and glorify the labors of this mighty investigator." Here Tyndall is using the word "philosopher" in its old sense, to mean "man of science." Speaking of the *man,* he said, "Not half his greatness was incorporate in his science, for science could not reveal the bravery and delicacy of his heart."

The material of the discourse was published in book form in the spring of 1868 under the title *Faraday as a Discoverer.* Before Tyndall's death in 1893 the reprinted book had appeared as a second edition, a third edition, a fourth edition, and was ready to be issued as a fifth edition.

Since the new edition of *Faraday as a Discoverer* is now being presented almost a hundred years after its original publication, it needs an explana-

tion of its background to make all points under-
standable.

THE ROYAL INSTITUTION
AND FARADAY'S RELATION TO IT

The Royal Institution of London was a unique
organization. It was founded in 1799 by Count
Rumford—who had been born in colonial America. It was intended, originally, to be a general
center for instruction in science, and to give practical applications of science in the trades. The
building designed for the work had a large lecture
hall, a library, and a great deal of laboratory space.
On the floor above was an apartment for the superintendent and two rooms for an assistant.

The appointment of Humphry Davy as superintendent was to bring about a modification of the
original plan. This was not because Davy had any
objection to working with tradesmen but because,
as a brilliant young scientist, he had so many things
that he wished to experiment upon. Through his
efforts the main laboratory of the Institution became the best-equipped research laboratory in
England. As a chemist, he made in that "work-
shop" (which is what the word *laboratory* means)
many new chemical substances. With the aid of
current from a newly built electric battery of voltaic cells, and a new chemical approach, he isolated

several completely new chemical elements: potassium, sodium, barium, strontium, calcium, and lithium. Davy was a wonderful and enthusiastic speaker and illustrated his lectures with striking experiments, so he drew large audiences to his public lectures in the lecture hall of the Institution.

Michael Faraday, when twenty-two, became Davy's laboratory assistant. A skillful instrument maker, deeply interested in science but without any formal training either in chemistry or in mathematics, he was used by Davy in routine testing and in keeping equipment in perfect condition. When Davy—who was now *Sir* Humphry Davy—and his wife spent a year and a half in Italy, young Faraday went along as his assistant with the research work at which Davy was always busy. In that year and a half, Faraday had a chance to meet many scientists, to read in Davy's library, to notice how research problems were attacked and carried through. Toward the end of that period he was encouraged to start a project of his own.

Returning with the Davys to London, he again became a laboratory assistant at the Institution. Soon he was asked to give his first lecture, soon his first research study was published. In 1821, when he was twenty-nine, he was appointed, on Davy's recommendation, to succeed the celebrated chemist as Superintendent of the House and Laboratory at the Royal Institution. Already recognized at that time as an able young scientist, he had been elected a fellow of that important scientific society, the Royal Society, of which Davy was then president.

Faraday now married Sarah Barnard. Moving from his rooms that he had used as an assistant, he and his bride took over the superintendent's apartment in the floor above the laboratory, which was to be their home for over forty years. After Davy's retirement Faraday was director of all experimental work and had an assistant to help him. In 1831 his projects began to center about the relation of electricity to magnetism, an almost completely new phase of science. The next four years were filled with completely original experimental work that Tyndall declares was of an amount unparalleled in the history of science. After that, other phases of electrical action were taken up—making a total so great that in *Faraday as a Discoverer* Tyndall uses several pages just to summarize it briefly.

JOHN TYNDALL AND HIS RELATIONS TO FARADAY AND THE ROYAL INSTITUTION

Tyndall reports that he saw Faraday for the first time in the summer of 1850. He was twenty-nine and Faraday was fifty-eight. He had been, however, quite familiar with Faraday's experimental work and was thrilled to meet him personally. In 1853, when he was thirty-two, Tyndall was offered the chair of physics at the Institution, on the recommendation of the older man. With that, there began what Tyndall was to count as "fifteen years of intimacy." In that period Faraday's wonderful series of researches on electricity and magnetism came to a close. And in it the great scientist retired, and the Faradays left their long-time home in the apartment on the floor above the laboratory. Yet for a few years after that, Tyndall reports that Faraday would each week slip into his accustomed place in the lecture hall of the Institution to listen to the Friday Evening Discourses—a weekly program largely given over to popular talks on science, which Faraday himself had started shortly after his appointment as superintendent. Finally the end came peacefully, so Tyndall writes, in August 1867. Against this background of intimacy and understanding his memorial discourse was given.

Woven into the memorial material are incidental references to points in Tyndall's own career. When he remarks, "You might not credit me were I to tell you how lightly I value the honor of being

Faraday's successor compared with the honor of being Faraday's friend," he is alluding to the fact known to all his listening audience that he had taken Faraday's place as lecturer for the Trinity House school and science advisor for the National Board of Trade, as well as Superintendent of the Royal Institution and Director of the Laboratories.

There are some notations about his own research activities woven into the story. He comments briefly about the two years at a German university. "Drawn by the fame of Bunsen as a teacher, in the year 1848 I became a student at the University of Marburg, in Hesse Cassel." There is a further notation about a third year's work in Germany, this time in the laboratory of Professor Magnus of Berlin, on diamagnetism and magnecrystallic action. "I returned to Germany, worked there for nearly another year, and in June 1851 came back finally from Berlin to England."

He puts down no facts about his life before going to Germany. From other sources it is known that he was born in Ireland in the summer of 1820. In his childhood he attended the village school. When nineteen he carried the chain for a surveying group. In a few years he had charge of the group, made the maps, and worked out complex calculations in engineering. He was very good at mathematics. Then came three years in practical rail-road building. As hobby interests, he became fascinated with geology, from noting the strata through which the railroad cuts were made, and in the wild flowers and plants of Ireland.

From Ireland he went to Queenswood College in Hampshire, England, as a teacher of science. His own knowledge of science was largely self-taught but he was a fine teacher. The head of the school said he was "a regular firebrand of enthusiasm." In the year that he was there, Tyndall was making experiments upon magnets. While railroading he had saved up four hundred pounds. With this equivalent of two thousand dollars, he set out for Marburg University in Germany, there to spend two years. In his second year he was lecture assistant to the great German chemist Robert Bunsen. When he was appointed to the Royal Institution in London in 1853, a fact already mentioned, he was described as tall, thin, bronzed, animated—and quoting the German of Bunsen with an Irish accent.

At the Institution he was noted both for his research activities and his lectures. In the period from 1859 to 1871 his research work was on the transparency and opacity of gases and vapors for radiant heat. This work was of great importance.

In the period from 1863 to 1873 five books of his appeared that had been previously given as groups of two or more lectures. In addition to *Faraday as a Discoverer* (1868), these were *Heat as a Mode of Motion* (1863), *On Sound* (1867), *The Forms of Water* (1872), and *Lectures on Light* (1873).

The last of these—the *Lectures on Light*—were given in a lecture tour in the United States in 1872–3. Taking with him an abundance of apparatus and three assistants, Tyndall gave a series of six lectures on light at all the major colleges. In addition, he gave popular lectures on science subjects in the main large cities in the eastern part of the United States. These popular-science addresses were given to packed houses everywhere. About Tyndall as a lecturer, one American listener wrote, "He was a most fascinating speaker, fluent, direct, easy, his whole discourse well seasoned with humor." The lecture tour was a great success and netted $13,000, the whole amount of which Tyndall donated as a fund to be used for the advancement of natural science in America.

Tyndall died in his home, Hind Head House, England, in 1893. In 1877 he had built a cottage on Bel Alp above the Rhone Valley and had spent most of the intervening years, in England or in

Switzerland, as a partial invalid. A few days before his death he wrote the preface for the fifth edition of *Faraday as a Discoverer,* a book that had been published originally twenty-five years before.

In the handling of those five editions one can sense the change of readers for this great book. The first edition carried no preface. It needed none, for the matters it spoke of were of current interest. A great scientist had died and this was a memorial to his importance.

The preface for the second edition was written in December 1869. Almost two years had passed since the first publication. Students were using the book as supplementary reading. Tyndall has a message for them in the preface. The opening paragraph of that preface reads, "The experimental researches of Faraday are so voluminous, their descriptions are so detailed, and their wealth of illustration is so great, as to render it a heavy labor to master them. The multiplication of proofs, necessary and interesting when the new truths had to be established, are however less needful now when the new truths have become household words in science. I have therefore tried in the following pages to compress the body, without injury to the spirit, of these imperishable investigations, and to present them in a form which should be convenient and useful to the student of the present day."

This might give the impression that the second edition was more compressed than the original one had been. It wasn't. The texts of the two were completely alike.

The third edition carried no new preface. But for the republished book of 1884—issued sixteen years after the first printing—the reading audience has changed. One sentence of the brief new preface for this fourth edition reads, ". . . it seemed to me that the labors, and points of character, of so great a worker and so good a man should not be allowed to vanish from the public eye."

Finally, in December 1893 Tyndall wrote the preface for the fifth edition. By this time the telegraph, telephone, electric lighting, and electric power developments had become so commonplace that the research activities that had made these electrical devices possible were becoming forgotten. He wants to remind the reader that the developments had their "origin in the discoveries made by Michael Faraday, sixty-two years ago." As he looks over the proofs of the new edition he is "confirmed in the conviction that the book ought not to be suffered to go out of print."

The present edition is a republished form of the fifth edition. It has retained the preface written in 1893. Earlier prefaces have not been included. His wife had added a note to the 1893 preface which explains the matter. "It was, I believe, my husband's intention to substitute this preface, written a few days before his death, for all former prefaces."

The new edition has made no change in the original wording. It has kept the footnotes added by Tyndall as he prepared the material of 1868 for the printer. For the readers of today, separated both by time and country from the England of almost a century ago, some notes and an appendix have been prepared and a few illustrations added.

There is a final comment on this scientific classic. What we call science, and in particular physics, was generally referred to in the days of a century ago as *natural philosophy*. So, in this book, a *philosopher* means a scientist. In Scottish universities the department of physics is still called the department of natural philosophy.

July, 1960

Preface to the Fifth Edition

DAILY AND weekly, from all parts of the world, I receive publications bearing upon the practical applications of electricity. This great movement, the ultimate outcome of which is not to be foreseen, had its origin in the discoveries made by Michael Faraday sixty-two years ago. From these discoveries have sprung applications of the telephone order, together with various forms of the electric telegraph. From them have sprung the extraordinary advances made in electrical illumination. Faraday could have had but an imperfect notion of the expansions of which his discoveries were capable. Still he had a vivid and strong imagination, and I do not doubt that he saw possibilities which did not disclose themselves to the general scientific mind. He knew that his discoveries had their practical side, but he steadfastly resisted the seductions of this side, applying himself to the development of principles; being well aware that the practical question would receive due development hereafter.

During my sojourn in Switzerland this year, I read through the proofs of this new edition, and by my reading was confirmed in the conviction that the book ought not to be suffered to go out of print. The memoir was written under great pressure, but I am not ashamed of it as it stands. Glimpses of Faraday's character and gleams of his discoveries are there to be found which will be of interest to humanity to the end of time.

JOHN TYNDALL

HIND HEAD,
December, 1893

Contents

CONTENTS

Faraday
AS A DISCOVERER

Parentage; Introduction to the Royal Institution; Earliest Experiments; First Royal Society Paper; Marriage

IT HAS been thought desirable to give you and the world some image of Michael Faraday as a scientific investigator and discoverer. The attempt to respond to this desire has been to me a labor of difficulty, if also a labor of love. For however well acquainted I may be with the researches and discoveries of that great master, however numerous the illustrations which occur to me of the loftiness of Faraday's character and the beauty of his life— still to grasp him and his researches as a whole; to seize upon the ideas which guided him, and connected them; to gain entrance into that strong and active brain, and read from it the riddle of the world—this is a work not easy of performance, and all but impossible amid the distraction of duties of another kind. That I should at one period or another speak to you regarding Faraday and his work is natural, if not inevitable; but I did not expect to be called upon to speak so soon. Still the bare suggestion that this is the fit and proper time for speech sent me immediately to my task; from it I have returned with such results as I could gather, and also with the wish that those results were more worthy than they are of the greatness of my theme.

It is not my intention to lay before you a *life* of Faraday in the ordinary acceptation of the term. The duty I have to perform is to give you some notion of what he has done in the world, dwelling incidentally on the spirit in which his work was executed, and introducing such personal traits as may be necessary to the completion of your picture of the *philosopher*, though by no means adequate to give you a complete idea of the *man*.

The newspapers have already informed you that Michael Faraday was born at Newington Butts, on September 22, 1791, and that he died at Hampton Court, on August 25, 1867. Believing, as I do, in the general truth of the doctrine of hereditary transmission—sharing the opinion of Mr. Carlyle, that "a really able man never proceeded from entirely stupid parents"—I once used the privilege of my intimacy with Mr. Faraday to ask him whether his parents showed any signs of unusual ability. He could remember none. His father, I believe, was a great sufferer during the latter years of his life, and this might have masked whatever intellectual power he possessed. When thirteen years old, that is to say in 1804, Faraday was apprenticed to a bookseller and bookbinder in Blandford Street, Manchester Square; here he spent eight years of his life, after which he worked as a journeyman elsewhere.

You have also heard the account of Faraday's first contact with the Royal Institution; that he was introduced by one of the members to Sir Humphry Davy's last lectures, that he took notes of those lectures, wrote them fairly out, and sent them to Davy, entreating him at the same time to enable him to quit trade, which he detested, and to pursue science, which he loved. Davy was helpful to the young man, and this should never be forgotten; he at once wrote to Faraday, and afterwards, when an opportunity occurred, made

him his assistant.* Mr. Gassiot has lately favored
me with the following reminiscence of this time:

Clapham Common, Surrey
November 28, 1867.

My Dear Tyndall—Sir H. Davy was accustomed to
call on the late Mr. Pepys, in the Poultry, on his way
to the London Institution, of which Pepys was one of
the original managers. The latter told me that on one
occasion Sir H. Davy, showing him a letter, said:
"Pepys, what am I to do, here is a letter from a young
man named Faraday; he has been attending my lectures, and wants me to give him employment at the
Royal Institution. *What can I do?*" "*Do?*" replied
Pepys, "put him to wash bottles; if he is good for anything he will do it directly, if he refuses he is good for

---

* Here is Davy's recommendation of Faraday, presented
to the managers of the Royal Institution, at a meeting on
the 18th of March, 1813, Charles Hatchett, Esq., in the
chair:

"Sir Humphry Davy has the honor to inform the managers that he has found a person who is desirous to occupy
the situation in the Institution lately filled by William Payne.
His name is Michael Faraday. He is a youth of twenty-two
years of age. As far as Sir H. Davy has been able to observe
or ascertain, he appears well fitted for the situation. His
habits seem good; his disposition active and cheerful, and his
manner intelligent. He is willing to engage himself on the
same terms as given to Mr. Payne at the time of quitting the
Institution.

"*Resolved*—That Michael Faraday be engaged to fill the
situation lately occupied by Mr. Payne, on the same terms."

nothing." "No, no," replied Davy, "we must try him with something better than that." The result was, that Davy engaged him to assist in the Laboratory at *weekly* wages.

Davy held the joint office of Professor of Chemistry and Director of the Laboratory; he ultimately gave up the former to the late Professor Brande, but he insisted that Faraday should be appointed Director of the Laboratory, and, as Faraday told me, this enabled him on subsequent occasions to hold a definite position in the Institution, in which he was always supported by Davy. I believe he held that office to the last.

Believe me, my dear Tyndall, yours truly,

J. P. GASSIOT

From a letter written by Faraday himself soon after his appointment as Davy's assistant, I extract the following account of his introduction to the Royal Institution:

London, Sept. 13, 1813.

As for myself, I am absent (from home) nearly day and night, except occasional calls, and it is likely shall shortly be absent entirely, but this (having nothing more to say, and at the request of my mother) I will explain to you. I was formerly a bookseller and binder, but am now turned philosopher,* which happened thus: Whilst an apprentice, I, for amusement, learnt a little chemistry and other parts of philosophy, and felt an

---

* Faraday loved this word and employed it to the last; he had an intense dislike to the modern term *physicist*.

eager desire to proceed in that way further. After being a journeyman for six months, under a disagreeable master, I gave up my business, and through the interest of a Sir H. Davy, filled the situation of chemical assistant to the Royal Institution of Great Britain, in which office I now remain; and where I am constantly employed in observing the works of nature, and tracing the manner in which she directs the order and arrangement of the world. I have lately had proposals made to me by Sir Humphry Davy to accompany him in his travels through Europe and Asia, as philosophical assistant. If I go at all I expect it will be in October next—about the end; and my absence from home will perhaps be as long as three years. But as yet all is uncertain.

This account is supplemented by the following letter, written by Faraday to his friend De la Rive,* on the occasion of the death of Mrs. Marcet. The letter is dated September 2, 1858:

My Dear Friend—Your subject interested me deeply every way; for Mrs. Marcet was a good friend to me, as she must have been to many of the human race. I entered the shop of a bookseller and bookbinder at the age of thirteen, in the year 1804, remained there eight years, and during the chief part of my time bound books. Now it was in those books, in the hours after work, that I found the beginning of my philosophy. There were two that especially helped me, the *Ency-*

_____
* To whom I am indebted for a copy of the original letter.

clopaedia Britannica, from which I gained my first notions of electricity, and Mrs. Marcet's *Conversation on Chemistry,* which gave me my foundation in that science.

Do not suppose that I was a very deep thinker, or was marked as a precocious person. I was a very lively imaginative person, and could believe in the *Arabian Nights* as easily as in the *Encyclopaedia.* But facts were important to me, and saved me. I could trust a fact, and always cross-examined an assertion. So when I questioned Mrs. Marcet's book by such little experiments as I could find means to perform, and found it true to the facts as I could understand them, I felt that I had got hold of an anchor in chemical knowledge, and clung fast to it. Thence my deep veneration for Mrs. Marcet—first as one who had conferred great personal good and pleasure on me; and then as one able to convey the truth and principle of those boundless fields of knowledge which concern natural things to the young, untaught, and inquiring mind.

You may imagine my delight when I came to know Mrs. Marcet personally; how often I cast my thoughts backward, delighting to connect the past and the present; how often, when sending a paper to her as a thank offering, I thought of my first instructress, and such like thoughts will remain with me.

I have some such thoughts even as regards *your own father;* who was, I may say, the first who personally at Geneva, and afterwards by correspondence, encouraged, and by that sustained me.

Twelve or thirteen years ago Mr. Faraday and myself quitted the Institution one evening together, to pay a visit to our friend Grove in Baker Street. He took my arm at the door, and, pressing it to his side in his warm genial way, said, "Come, Tyndall, I will now show you something that will interest you." We walked northwards, passed the house of Mr. Babbage, which drew forth a reference to the famous evening parties once assembled there. We reached Blandford Street, and after a little looking about he paused before a stationer's shop, and then went in. On entering the shop, his usual animation seemed doubled; he looked rapidly at everything it contained. To the left on entering was a door, through which he looked down into a little room, with a window in front facing Blandford Street. Drawing me towards him, he said eagerly, "Look there, Tyndall, that was my working place. I bound books in that little nook." A respectable-looking woman stood behind the counter: his conversation with me was too low to be heard by her, and he now turned to the counter to buy some cards as an excuse for our being there. He asked the woman her name—her predecessor's name—his predecessor's name. "That won't do," he said, with good-humored impatience; "who was *his* predecessor?" "Mr. Riebau," she replied, and immediately added, as if suddenly recollecting herself, "He, sir, was the master of Sir Charles Faraday." "Nonsense!" he responded, "there is no such person." Great was her delight when I told her the name of her visitor; but she assured me that as soon as she saw him running about the shop, she felt—though she did not know why—that it must be "Sir Charles Faraday."

Faraday did, as you know, accompany Davy to Rome; he was re-engaged by the managers of the Royal Institution on May 15, 1815. Here he made rapid progress in chemistry, and after a time was entrusted with easy analyses by Davy. In those days the Royal Institution published *The Quarterly Journal of Science,* the precursor of our own *Proceedings.* Faraday's first contribution to science appeared in that journal in 1816. It was an analysis of some caustic lime from Tuscany, which had been sent to Davy by the Duchess of Montrose. Between this period and 1818 various notes and short papers were published by Faraday. In 1818 he experimented upon "sounding flames." Professor Auguste De la Rive had investigated those sounding flames, and had applied to them an explanation which completely accounted for a class of sounds discovered by himself, but did not account for those known to his predecessors. By a few simple and conclusive experiments, Faraday proved the explanation insufficient. It is an epoch in the life of a young man when he finds himself correcting a person of eminence, and in Faraday's case, where its effect was to develop a modest self-trust, such an event could not fail to act profitably.

From time to time between 1818 and 1820 Faraday published scientific notes and notices of minor weight. At this time he was acquiring, not producing; working hard for his master and storing and strengthening his own mind. He assisted Mr. Brande in his lectures, and so quietly, skilfully, and modestly was his work done, that Mr. Brande's vocation at the time was pronounced "lecturing on velvet." In 1820 Faraday published a chemical paper "on two new compounds of chlorine and carbon, and on a new compound of iodine, carbon, and hydrogen." This paper was read before the Royal Society on December 21, 1820, and it was the first of his that was honored with a place in the *Philosophical Transactions*.

On June 12, 1821, he married, and obtained leave to bring his young wife into his rooms at the Royal Institution. There for forty-six years they lived together, occupying the suite of apartments which had been previously in the successive occupancy of Young, Davy, and Brande. At the time of her marriage Mrs. Faraday was twenty-one years of age, he being nearly thirty. Regarding this marriage I will at present limit myself to quoting an entry written in Faraday's own hand in his book of diplomas, which caught my eye while in his company some years ago. It ran thus:

25th January, 1847.

Amongst these records and events, I here insert the date of one which, as a source of honor and happiness, far exceeds all the rest. We were *married* on June 12, 1821.

M. FARADAY

Then follows the copy of the minutes, dated May 21, 1821, which gave him additional rooms, and thus enabled him to bring his wife to the Royal Institution. A feature of Faraday's character which I have often noticed makes itself apparent in this entry. In his relations to his wife he added *chivalry* to affection.

Early Researches; Magnetic Rotations;
Liquefaction of Gases; Heavy Glass;
Charles Anderson; Contributions
to Physics

Oersted, in 1820, discovered the action of a voltaic current on a magnetic needle; and immediately afterwards the splendid intellect of Ampère succeeded in showing that every magnetic phenomenon then known might be reduced to the mutual action of electric currents. The subject occupied all men's thought; and in this country Dr. Wollaston sought to convert the deflection of the needle by the current into a permanent *rotation* of the needle round the current. He also hoped to produce the reciprocal effect of causing a current to rotate round a magnet. In the early part

12

of 1821, Wollaston attempted to realize this idea in the presence of Sir Humphry Davy in the laboratory of the Royal Institution. This was well calculated to attract Faraday's attention to the subject. He read much about it; and in the months of July, August, and September he wrote a *History of the Progress of Electromagnetism*, which he published in Thomson's *Annals of Philosophy*. Soon afterwards he took up the subject of "magnetic rotations," and on the morning of Christmas Day, 1821, he called his wife to witness, for the first time, the revolution of a magnetic needle round an electric current. Incidental to the "historic sketch," he repeated almost all the experiments there referred to; and these, added to his own subsequent work, made him practical master of all that was then known regarding the voltaic current. In 1821, he also touched upon a subject

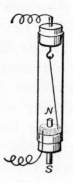

Faraday's electromagnetic rotation apparatus, designed in January, 1822. It was made of a piece of glass tubing, with stoppers at each end. The lower stopper carried a magnet and a pool of mercury. A loose piece of platinum wire, hung by a loop from the top connection, revolved rapidly around the magnet pole when the outside current was connected to the wire terminals of the apparatus.

which subsequently received his closer attention—
the vaporization of mercury at common tempera-
tures; and immediately afterwards conducted, in
company with Mr. Stodart, experiments on the
alloys of steel. He was accustomed in after years
to present to his friends razors formed from one
of the alloys then discovered.

During Faraday's hours of liberty from other
duties, he took up subjects of inquiry for himself;
and in the spring of 1823, thus self-prompted, he
began the examination of a substance which had
long been regarded as the chemical element chlorine, in a solid form, but which Sir Humphry
Davy, in 1810, had proved to be a hydrate of
chlorine, that is, a compound of chlorine and
water. Faraday first analyzed this hydrate, and
wrote out an account of its composition. This
account was looked over by Davy, who suggested
the heating of the hydrate under pressure in
a sealed glass tube. This was done. The hydrate
fused at a blood heat, the tube became filled
with a yellow atmosphere, and was afterwards
found to contain two liquid substances. Dr.
Paris happened to enter the laboratory while
Faraday was at work. Seeing the oily liquid
in his tube, he rallied the young chemist for
his carelessness in employing soiled vessels. On filing

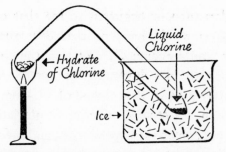

Faraday's apparatus for liquefying the gas chlorine produced the gas by heating the hydrate. Both chlorine and water vapor were formed, thus giving pressure within the tube. At the right the tube was cooled with ice. The combination of pressure with cooling changed the chlorine to a liquid.

off the end of the tube, its contents exploded and the oily matter vanished. Early next morning, Dr. Paris received the following note:

Dear Sir—The *oil* you noticed yesterday turns out to be liquid chlorine.

Yours faithfully,
M. FARADAY *

The gas had been liquefied by its own pressure. Faraday then tried compression with a syringe, and succeeded thus in liquefying the gas.

To the published account of this experiment Davy added the following note: "In desiring Mr. Faraday to expose the hydrate of chlorine in a

---

* Paris, *Life of Davy,* page 391.

closed glass tube, it occurred to me that one of
three things would happen: that decomposition
of water would occur; . . . or that the chlorine
would separate in a fluid state." Davy, moreover,
immediately applied the method of self-compress-
ing atmosphere to the liquefaction of muriatic gas.
Faraday continued the experiments, and succeeded
in reducing a number of gases till then deemed
permanent to the liquid condition. In 1844 he returned to the subject, and considerably expanded
its limits. These important investigations established the fact that gases are but the vapors of
liquids possessing a very low boiling point, and
gave a sure basis to our views of molecular aggregation. The account of the first investigation was
read before the Royal Society on April 10, 1823,
and was published, in Faraday's name, in the *Philosophical Transactions*. The second memoir was
sent to the Royal Society on December 19, 1844.
I may add that while he was conducting his first
experiments on the liquefaction of gases, thirteen
pieces of glass were on one occasion driven by an
explosion into Faraday's eye.

Some small notices and papers, including the
observation that glass readily changes color in sun-
light, follow here. In 1825 and 1826 Faraday published papers in the *Philosophical Transactions* on

"new compounds of carbon and hydrogen," and on "sulphonaphthalic acid." In the former of these papers he announced the discovery of benzol,[1] * which, in the hands of modern chemists, has become the foundation of our splendid aniline dyes. But he swerved incessantly from chemistry into physics; and in 1826 we find him engaged in investigating the limits of vaporization, and showing, by exceedingly strong and apparently conclusive arguments, that even in the case of mercury such a limit exists; much more he conceived it to be certain that our atmosphere does not contain the vapor of the fixed constituents of the earth's crust. This question, I may say, is likely to remain an open one. Dr. Rankine, for example, has lately drawn attention to the odor of certain metals; whence comes this odor, if it be not from the vapor of the metal?

In 1825 Faraday became a member of a committee, to which Sir John Herschel and Mr. Dollond also belonged, appointed by the Royal Society to examine, and if possible improve, the manufacture of glass for optical purposes. Their experiments continued till 1829, when the account of them constituted the subject of a "Bakerian Lecture." This lectureship, founded in 1774 by

---

* Numbered reference notes begin on page 202.

Henry Baker, Esq., of the Strand, London, provides that every year a lecture shall be given before the Royal Society, the sum of four pounds being paid to the lecturer. The Bakerian Lecture, however, has long since passed from the region of pay to that of honor, papers of mark only being chosen for it by the council of the Society. Faraday's first Bakerian Lecture, "On the Manufacture of Glass for Optical Purposes," was delivered at the close of 1829. It is a most elaborate and conscientious description of processes, precautions, and results; the details were so exact and so minute, and the paper consequently so long, that three successive sittings of the Royal Society were taken up by the delivery of the lecture.* This glass did not turn out to be of important practical use,† but

---

* Viz., November 19, December 3 and 10.

† I make the following extract from a letter from Sir John Herschel, written to me from Collingwood, on the 3rd of November, 1867:

"I will take this opportunity to mention that I believe myself to have originated the suggestion of the employment of borate of lead for *optical* purposes. It was somewhere in the year 1822, as well as I can recollect, that I mentioned it to Sir James (then Mr.) South; and, in consequence, the trial was made in his laboratory in Blackman Street, by precipitating and working a large quantity of borate of lead, and fusing it under a muffle in a porcelain evaporating dish. A very limpid (though slightly yellow) glass resulted, the refractive index 1.866! (which you will find set down in my table of

it happened afterwards to be the foundation of two of Faraday's greatest discoveries.

The experiments here referred to were commenced at the Falcon Glass Works, on the premises of Messrs. Green and Pellatt, but Faraday could not conveniently attend to them there. In 1827, therefore, a furnace was erected in the yard of the Royal Institution; and it was at this time, and with a view of assisting him at the furnace, that Faraday engaged Sergeant Anderson, of the Royal Artillery, the respectable, truthful, and altogether trustworthy man whose appearance here is so fresh in our memories. Anderson continued to be the reverential helper of Faraday and the faithful servant of this Institution for nearly forty years.*

---

refractive indices in my article 'Light,' *Encyclopaedia Metropolitana*). It was, however, too soft for optical use as an object glass. This Faraday overcame, at least to a considerable degree, by the introduction of silica."

* Regarding Anderson, Faraday writes thus in 1845: "I cannot resist the occasion that is thus offered to me of mentioning the name of Mr. Anderson, who came to me as an assistant in the glass experiments, and has remained ever since in the laboratory of the Royal Institution. He assisted me in all the researches into which I have entered since that time; and to his care, steadiness, exactitude, and faithfulness in the performance of all that has been committed to his charge, I am much indebted.—M. F." (*Experimental Researches*, volume 3, page 3, footnote.)

In 1831 Faraday published a paper, "On a Peculiar Class of Optical Deceptions," to which I believe the beautiful optical toy called the chromatrope owes its origin. In the same year he published a paper on vibrating surfaces, in which he solved an acoustical problem which, though of extreme simplicity *when solved*, appears to have baffled many eminent men. The problem was to account for the fact that light bodies, such as the seed of lycopodium, collected at the vibrating parts of sounding plates, while sand ran to the nodal lines. Faraday showed that the light bodies were entangled in the little whirlwinds formed in the air over the places of vibration, and through which the heavier sand was readily projected. Faraday's resources as an experimentalist were so wonderful, and his delight in experiment was so great, that he sometimes almost ran into excess in this direction. I have heard him say that this paper on vibrating surfaces was too heavily laden with experiments.

*Discovery of Magnetoelectricity;
Explanation of Arago's Magnetism of
Rotation; Terrestrial Magnetoelectric
Induction; The Extra Current*

THE WORK thus referred to, though sufficient of itself to secure no mean scientific reputation, forms but the vestibule of Faraday's achievements. He had been engaged within these walls for eighteen years. During part of the time he had drunk in knowledge from Davy, and during the remainder he continually exercised his capacity for independent inquiry. In 1831 we have him at the climax of his intellectual strength, forty years of age, stored with knowledge and full of original power. Through reading, lecturing, and experimenting, he had become thoroughly familiar with electrical science; he saw where light was needed and expansion possible. The phenomena of ordinary electric induction belonged, as it were, to the alphabet of his knowledge; he knew that under ordinary circumstances the presence of an electrified body was sufficient to excite, by induction, an unelectrified body. He knew that the wire which carried an electric current was an electrified body, and still that all attempts had failed to make it excite in other wires a state similar to its own.

What was the reason of this failure? Faraday never could work from the experiments of others, however clearly described. He knew well that from every experiment issues a kind of radiation, luminous in different degrees to different minds, and he hardly trusted himself to reason upon an experiment that he had not seen. In the autumn of 1831 he began to repeat the experiments with electric currents, which, up to that time, had produced no positive result. And here, for the sake of younger inquirers, if not for the sake of us all, it is worth while to dwell for a moment on a power which Faraday possessed in an extraordinary degree. He united vast strength with perfect flexibility. His momentum was that of a river, which combines weight and directness with the ability to yield to the flexures of its bed. The intentness of his vision in any direction did not apparently diminish his power of perception in other directions; and when he attacked a subject, expecting results, he had the faculty of keeping his mind alert, so that results different from those which he expected should not escape him through preoccupation.

He began his experiments on the induction of electric currents by composing a helix of two insulated wires which were wound side by side round the same wooden cylinder. One of these wires he connected with a voltaic battery of ten cells, and the other with a sensitive galvanometer. When connection with the battery was made, and while the current flowed, no effect whatever was observed at the galvanometer. But he never accepted an experimental result until he had applied to it the utmost power at his command. He raised his battery from 10 cells to 120 cells, but without avail. The current flowed calmly through the battery wire without producing, during its flow, any sensible result upon the galvanometer.

"During its flow," and this was the time when an effect was expected—but here Faraday's power of lateral vision, separating, as it were, from the

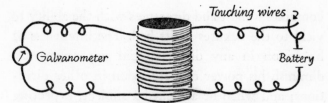

Two completely independent coils of insulated wire were wound side by side on a wooden cylinder. One coil was connected to a voltaic battery, the current flowing when the battery wires were touched together. The other coil was connected to a sensitive galvanometer. At the moment that the battery wires were touched, the galvanometer moved, though the circuits were separate.

line of expectation, came into play. He noticed that a feeble movement of the needle always occurred at the moment when he made contact with the battery; that the needle would afterwards return to its fomer position and remain quietly there unaffected by the *flowing* current. At the moment, however, when the circuit was interrupted the needle again moved, and in a direction opposed to that observed on the completion of the circuit.

This result, and others of a similar kind, led him to the conclusion that the battery current through the one wire did in reality induce a similar current through the other; but that it continued for an instant only, and partook more of the nature of the electric wave from a common Leyden jar than of the current from a voltaic battery. The momentary currents thus generated were called *induced* currents, while the current which generated them was called the *inducing* current. It was immediately proved that the current generated at making the circuit was always opposed in direction to its generator, while that developed on the rupture of the circuit coincided in direction with the inducing current. It appeared as if the current on its first rush through the primary wire sought a purchase in the secondary one, and, by a kind of kick, impelled backward through the latter an electric wave, which subsided as soon as the primary current was fully established.

Faraday, for a time, believed that the secondary wire, though quiescent when the primary current had been once established, was not in its natural condition, its return to that condition being declared by the current observed at breaking the circuit. He called this hypothetical state of the wire the *electrotonic state;* he afterwards abandoned this hypothesis, but seemed to return to it in later life. The term electrotonic is also preserved by Professor Du Bois Reymond to express a certain electric condition of the nerves, and Professor Clerk Maxwell has ably defined and illustrated the hypothesis in the Tenth Volume of the

Transactions of the Cambridge Philosophical Society.

The mere approach of a wire forming a closed curve to a second wire through which a voltaic current flowed was then shown by Faraday to be sufficient to arouse in the neutral wire an induced current, opposed in direction to the inducing current; the withdrawal of the wire also generated a current having the same direction as the inducing current; those currents existed only during the time of approach or withdrawal, and when neither the primary nor the secondary wire was in motion, no matter how close their proximity might be, no induced current was generated.

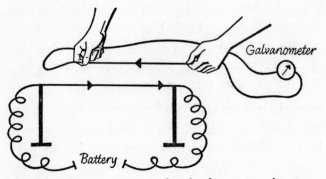

An induced current was produced when a wire forming a closed circuit through a galvanometer was brought near a wire carrying a voltaic current. The direction of the induced current was opposed to that of the inducing current.

Faraday has been called a purely inductive philosopher. A great deal of nonsense is, I fear, uttered in this land of England about induction and deduction. Some profess to befriend the one, some the other, while the real vocation of an investigator, like Faraday, consists in the incessant marriage of both. He was at this time full of the theory of Ampère, and it cannot be doubted that numbers of his experiments were executed merely to test his deductions from that theory. Starting from the discovery of Oersted, the illustrious French philosopher had shown that all the phenomena of magnetism then known might be reduced to the mutual attractions and repulsions of electric currents. Magnetism had been produced from electricity, and Faraday, who all his life long entertained a strong belief in such reciprocal actions, now attempted to effect the evolution of electricity from magnetism. Round a welded iron ring he placed two distinct coils of covered wire, causing the coils to occupy opposite halves of the ring. Connecting the ends of one of the coils with a galvanometer, he found that the moment the ring was magnetized, by sending a current through *the other coil,* the galvanometer needle whirled round four or five times in succession. The action, as before, was that of a pulse, which vanished

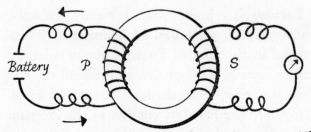

Two coils, P and S, were wound on an iron ring. The primary coil, P, was connected to a battery; the secondary coil, S, to a galvanometer. When a current was started in P, a current was induced in S in a direction opposite to that in P. With the current flowing in P, there was no current in S. When the current in P was interrupted, there was a reverse current in S.

immediately. On interrupting the circuit, a whirl of the needle in the opposite direction occurred. It was only during the time of magnetization or demagnetization that these effects were produced. The induced currents declared a *change* of condition only, and they vanished the moment the act of magnetization or demagnetization was complete.

The effects obtained with the welded ring were also obtained with straight bars of iron. Whether the bars were magnetized by the electric current, or were excited by the contact of permanent steel magnets, induced currents were always generated during the rise, and during the subsidence of the

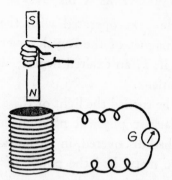

An induced current was produced by the mere motion of a permanent steel magnet in a coil of wire. A rush of electricity through the coil occurred when the magnet was inserted. An equal rush in the opposite direction occurred when the magnet was withdrawn.

magnetism. The use of iron was then abandoned, and the same effects were obtained by merely thrusting a permanent steel magnet into a coil of wire. A rush of electricity through the coil accompanied the insertion of the magnet; an equal rush in the opposite direction accompanied its withdrawal. The precision with which Faraday describes these results, and the completeness with which he defines the boundaries of his facts, are wonderful. The magnet, for example, must not be passed quite through the coil, but only half through; for if passed wholly through, the needle is stopped as by a blow, and then he shows how this blow results from a reversal of the electric wave in the helix. He next operated with the powerful permanent magnet of the Royal Society, and obtained with it, in an exalted degree, all the foregoing phenomena.

And now he turned the light of these discoveries upon the darkest physical phenomenon of that day. Arago had discovered, in 1824, that a disk of nonmagnetic metal had the power of bringing a vibrating magnetic needle suspended over it rapidly to rest; and that on causing the disk to rotate the magnetic needle rotated along with it. When both were quiescent, there was not the slightest measurable attraction or repulsion exerted between the needle and the disk; still, when in motion the disk was competent to drag after it not only a light needle, but a heavy magnet. The question had been probed and investigated with admirable skill by both Arago and Ampère, and Poisson had published a theoretic memoir on the subject; but no cause could be assigned for so extraordinary an action. It had also been examined in this country by two celebrated men, Mr. Babbage and Sir John Herschel; but it still remained a mystery. Faraday always recommended the suspension of judgment in cases of doubt. "I have always admired," he said, "the prudence and philosophical reserve shown by M. Arago in resisting the temptation to give a theory of the effect he had discovered, so long as he could not devise one which was perfect in its application, and in refusing to assent to the imperfect theories of others." Now, however, the time for theory had come. Faraday saw mentally the rotating disk, under the operation of the magnet, flooded with his induced currents, and from the known laws of interaction between currents and magnets he hoped to deduce the motion observed by Arago. That hope he realized, showing by actual experiment that, when his disk rotated, currents passed through it, their position and direction being such as must, in accordance with the established laws of electromagnetic action, produce the observed rotation.

Introducing the edge of his disk between the

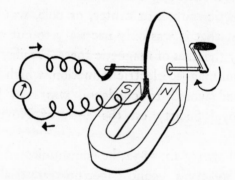

Faraday's electrical generator to produce a steady current by rotating a copper disk between the poles of a magnet.

poles of the large horseshoe magnet of the Royal Society, and connecting the axis and the edge of the disk, each by a wire with a galvanometer, he obtained, when the disk was turned round, a constant flow of electricity. The direction of the current was determined by the direction of the motion, the current being reversed when the rotation was reversed. He now states the law which rules the production of currents in both disks and wires, and in so doing used, for the first time, a phrase which has since become famous. When iron filings are scattered over a magnet, the particles of iron arrange themselves in certain determinate lines called magnetic curves. In 1831, Faraday for the first time called these curves "lines of magnetic force"; and he showed that to produce induced currents neither approach to nor withdrawal from a magnetic source, or center, or pole, was essential, but that it was only necessary to cut appropriately the lines of magnetic force. Faraday's first paper on magnetoelectric induction, which I have here endeavored to condense, was read before the Royal Society on the 24th of November, 1831.

On January 12, 1832, he communicated to the Royal Society a second paper on terrestrial magnetoelectric induction, which was chosen as the

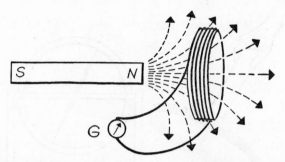

Lines of magnetic force pass out of the north pole of a magnet, and in at the south pole. To produce induced currents in a coil it was only necessary to cut appropriately the lines of magnetic force. For the arrangement shown, the coil may be spun around on its vertical axis or drawn back and forth across the end of the magnet.

Bakerian Lecture for the year. He placed a bar of iron in a coil of wire, and lifting the bar into the direction of the dipping needle, he excited by this action a current in the coil. On reversing the bar, a current in the opposite direction rushed through the wire. The same effect was produced when, on holding the helix in the line of dip, a bar of iron was thrust into it. Here, however, the earth acted on the coil through the intermediation of the bar of iron. He abandoned the bar and simply set a copper plate spinning in a horizontal plane; he knew that the earth's lines of magnetic force then crossed the plate at an angle of about 70°. When the plate spun round, the lines of force were inter-

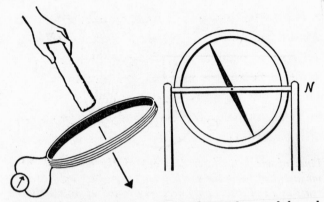

A dipping needle, shown in the background, is so balanced that it points slantingly downward toward the earth's north magnetic pole. (At Washington, D. C., the inclination, or dip, is 70 degrees.) Faraday found that, when an iron bar was thrust into a coil in the direction of the dip, a momentary current was induced.

sected and induced currents generated, which produced their proper effect when carried from the plate to the galvanometer. "When the plate was in the magnetic meridian, or in any other plane coinciding with the magnetic dip, then its rotation produced no effect upon the galvanometer."

At the suggestion of a mind fruitful in suggestions of a profound and philosophic character—I mean that of Sir John Herschel—Mr. Barlow, of Woolwich, had experimented with a rotating iron shell. Mr. Christie had also performed an elaborate series of experiments on a rotating iron disk. Both of them had found that when in rotation the body exercised a peculiar action upon the magnetic needle, deflecting it in a manner which was not observed during quiescence; but neither of them was aware at the time of the agent which produced this extraordinary deflection. They ascribed it to some change in the magnetism of the iron shell and disk.

But Faraday at once saw that his induced currents must come into play here, and he immediately obtained them from an iron disk. With a hollow brass ball, moreover, he produced the effects obtained by Mr. Barlow. Iron was in no way necessary; the only condition of success was that the rotating body should be of a character to admit of the formation of currents in its substance; it must, in other words, be a conductor of electricity. The higher the conducting power the more copious were the currents. He now passes from his little brass globe to the globe of the earth. He plays like a magician with the earth's magnetism. He sees the invisible lines along which its magnetic action is exerted, and sweeping his wand across these lines evokes this new power. Placing a simple loop of wire round a magnetic needle he bends its upper portion to the west; the north pole of the needle

immediately swerves to the east; he bends his loop
to the east, and the north pole moves to the west.
Suspending a common bar magnet in a vertical position, he causes it to spin round its own axis. Its
pole being connected with one end of a galvanometer wire, and its equator with the other end, electricity rushes round the galvanometer from the
rotating magnet. He remarks upon the *"singular
independence"* of the magnetism and the body of
the magnet which carries it. The steel behaves as if
it were isolated from its own magnetism.

And then his thoughts suddenly widen, and he
asks himself whether the rotating earth does not
generate induced currents as it turns round its
axis from west to east. In his experiment with the
twirling magnet the galvanometer wire remained
at rest; one portion of the circuit was in motion
relatively to *another portion*. But in the case of
the twirling planet the galvanometer wire would
necessarily be carried along with the earth; there
would be no relative motion. What must be the
consequence? Take the case of a telegraph wire
with its two terminal plates dipped into the earth,
and suppose the wire to lie in the magnetic meridian. The ground underneath the wire is influenced
like the wire itself by the earth's rotation; if a
current from south to north be generated in the

wire, a similar current from south to north would be generated in the earth under the wire; these currents would run against the same terminal plate, and thus neutralize each other.

This inference appears inevitable, but his profound vision perceived its possible invalidity. He saw that it was at least possible that the difference of conducting power between the earth and the wire might give one an advantage over the other, and that thus a residual or differential current might be obtained. He combined wires of different materials, and caused them to act in opposition to each other, but found the combination ineffectual. The more copious flow in the better conductor was exactly counterbalanced by the resistance of the worse. Still, though experiment was thus emphatic, he would clear his mind of all discomfort by operating on the earth itself. He went to the round lake near Kensington Palace, and stretched 480 feet of copper wire, north and south, over the lake, causing plates soldered to the wire at its ends to dip into the water. The copper wire was severed at the middle, and the severed ends connected with a galvanometer. No effect whatever was observed. But though quiescent water gave no effect, moving water might. He therefore worked at London Bridge for three days during the ebb and flow of the tide, but without any satisfactory result. Still he urges, "Theoretically it seems a necessary consequence, that where water is flowing there electric currents should be formed. If a line be imagined passing from Dover to Calais through the sea, and returning through the land, beneath the water to Dover, it traces out a circuit of conducting matter one part of which, when the water moves up or down the channel, is cutting the magnetic curves of the earth, whilst the other is relatively at rest. . . .

"There is every reason to believe that currents do run in the general direction of the circuit described, either one way or the other, according as the passage of the water is up or down the channel." This was written before the submarine cable was thought of, and he once informed me that actual observation upon that cable had been found to be in accordance with his theoretic deduction.*

---

* I am indebted to a friend for the following exquisite morsel: "A short time after the publication of Faraday's first researches in magnetoelectricity, he attended the meeting of the British Association at Oxford, in 1832. On this occasion he was requested by some of the authorities to repeat the celebrated experiment of eliciting a spark from a magnet, employing for this purpose the large magnet in the Ashmolean Museum. To this he consented, and a large party assembled to witness the experiments, which, I need not say, were perfectly successful. Whilst he was repeating them a

Three years subsequent to the publication of these researches—that is to say, on January 29, 1835—Faraday read before the Royal Society a paper "on the influence by induction of an electric current upon itself." A shock and spark of a peculiar character had been observed by a young man named William Jenkin, who must have been a youth of some scientific promise, but who, as Faraday once informed me, was dissuaded by his own father from having anything to do with science. The investigation of the fact noticed by Mr. Jenkin led Faraday to the discovery of the *extra current*, or the current *induced in the pri-*

---

dignitary of the University entered the room, and addressing himself to Professor Daniell, who was standing near Faraday, inquired what was going on. The Professor explained to him as popularly as possible this striking result of Faraday's great discovery. The Dean listened with attention and looked earnestly at the brilliant spark, but a moment after he assumed a serious countenance and shook his head; 'I am sorry for it,' said he, as he walked away. In the middle of the room he stopped for a moment and repeated, 'I am sorry for it,' then, walking towards the door, when the handle was in his hand he turned round and said, '*Indeed* I am sorry for it; it is putting new arms into the hands of the incendiary.' This occurred a short time after the papers had been filled with the doings of the hayrick burners. An erroneous statement of what fell from the Dean's mouth was printed at the time in one of the Oxford papers. He is there wrongly stated to have said, 'It is putting new arms into the hands of the infidel.' "

mary wire itself at the moments of making and breaking contact, the phenomena which he described and illustrated in the beautiful and exhaustive paper referred to.

Seven and thirty years have passed since the discovery of magnetoelectricity; but if we except the *extra current,* until quite recently nothing of moment was added to the subject. Faraday entertained the opinion that the discoverer of a great law of principle had a right to the "spoils"—this was his term—arising from its illustration; and guided by the principle he had discovered, his wonderful mind, aided by his wonderful ten fingers, overran in a single autumn this vast domain, and hardly left behind him the shred of a fact to be gathered by his successors.

And here the question may arise in some minds: What is the use of it all? The answer is, that if man's intellectual nature thirsts for knowledge, then knowledge is useful because it satisfies this thirst. If you demand practical ends, you must, I think, expand your definition of the term practical, and make it include all that elevates and enlightens the intellect, as well as all that ministers to the bodily health and comfort of men. Still, if needed, an answer of another kind might be given to the question "What is its use?" As far as electricity has been applied for medical purposes, it has been almost exclusively Faraday's electricity. You have noticed those lines of wire which cross the streets of London. It is Faraday's currents that speed from place to place through these wires. Approaching the point of Dungeness, the mariner sees an unusually brilliant light, and from the noble *phares* of La Hève the same light flashes across the sea. These are Faraday's sparks exalted by suitable machinery to sunlike splendor. At the present moment the Board of Trade and the Brethren of the Trinity House, as well as the Commissioners of Northern Lights, are contemplating the introduction of the magnetoelectric light at numerous points upon our coasts; and future generations will be able to refer to those guiding stars in answer to the question, what has been the practical use of the labors of Faraday? But I would again emphatically say, that his work needs no such justification, and that if he had allowed his vision to be disturbed by considerations regarding the practical use of his discoveries, those discoveries would never have been made by him. "I have rather," he writes in 1831, "been desirous of discovering new facts and new relations dependent on magnetoelectric induction, than of exalting the force of those already obtained, being assured that the latter would find their full development hereafter."

In 1817, when lecturing before a private society in London on the element chlorine, Faraday thus expressed himself with reference to this question of utility. "Before leaving this subject, I will point out the history of this substance, as an answer to those who are in the habit of saying to every new fact, 'What is its use?' Dr. Franklin says to such, 'What is the use of an infant?' The answer of the experimentalist is, 'Endeavor to make it useful.' When Scheele discovered this substance, it appeared to have no use; it was in its infancy and useless state, but having grown up to maturity, witness its powers, and see what endeavors to make it useful have done."

Points of Character

A POINT HIGHLY illustrative of the character of Faraday now comes into view. He gave an account of his discovery of magnetoelectricity in a letter to his friend M. Hachette, of Paris, who communicated the letter to the Academy of Sciences. The letter was translated and published; and immediately afterwards two distinguished Italian philosophers took up the subject, made numerous experiments, and published their results before the complete memoirs of Faraday had met the public eye. This evidently irritated him. He reprinted the paper of the learned Italians in the *Philosophical*

Magazine, accompanied by sharp critical notes from himself. He also wrote a letter dated December 1, 1832, to Gay-Lussac, who was then one of the editors of the *Annales de Chimie,* in which he analyzed the results of the Italian philosophers, pointing out their errors, and defending himself from what he regarded as imputations on his character. The style of this letter is unexceptionable, for Faraday could not write otherwise than as a gentleman; but the letter shows that had he willed it he could have hit hard. We have heard much of Faraday's gentleness and sweetness and tenderness. It is all true, but it is very incomplete. You cannot resolve a powerful nature into these elements, and Faraday's character would have been less admirable than it was had it not embraced forces and tendencies to which the silky adjectives "gentle" and "tender" would by no means apply. Underneath his sweetness and gentleness was the heat of a volcano. He was a man of excitable and fiery nature, but through high self-discipline he had converted the fire into a central glow and motive power of life, instead of permitting it to waste itself in useless passion. "He that is slow to anger," saith the sage, "is greater than the mighty, and he that ruleth his own spirit than he that taketh a city." [2] Faraday was *not* slow to anger, but he completely ruled his own spirit, and thus, though he took no cities, he captivated all hearts.

As already intimated, Faraday had contributed many of his minor papers—including his first analysis of caustic lime—to the *Quarterly Journal of Science*. In 1832, he collected those papers and others together in a small octavo volume, labeled them, and prefaced them thus:

PAPERS, NOTES, NOTICES, &c., &c.,
published in octavo,
up to 1832.
M. FARADAY.

Papers of mine, published in octavo, in the *Quarterly Journal of Science*, and elsewhere, since the time that Sir H. Davy encouraged me to write the analysis of caustic lime.

Some, I think (at this date), are good; others moderate; and some bad. But I have put *all* into the volume, because of the utility they have been of to me—and none more than the bad—in pointing out to me in future, or rather, after times, the faults it became me to watch and to avoid.

As I never looked over one of my papers a year after it was written without believing both in philosophy and manner it could have been much better done, I still hope the collection may be of great use to me.

M. FARADAY

August 18, 1832

"None more than the bad!" This is a bit of Faraday's innermost nature; and as I read these words I am almost constrained to retract what I have said regarding the fire and excitability of his character. But is he not all the more admirable, through his ability to tone down and subdue that fire and that excitability, so as to render himself able to write thus as a little child? I once took the liberty of censuring the conclusion of a letter of his to the Dean of Saint Paul's. He subscribed himself "humbly yours," and I objected to the adverb. "Well, but, Tyndall," he said, "I *am* humble; and still it would be a great mistake to think that I am not also proud." This duality ran through his character. A democrat in his defiance of all authority which unfairly limited his freedom of thought, and still ready to stoop in reverence to all that was really worthy of reverence, in the customs of the world or the characters of men.

And here, as well as elsewhere, may be introduced a letter which bears upon this question of self-control, written long years subsequent to the period at which we have now arrived. I had been at Glasgow in 1855, at a meeting of the British Association. On a certain day, I communicated a paper to the physical section, which was followed by a brisk discussion. Men of great distinction took part in it, the late Dr. Whewell among the number, and it waxed warm on both sides. I was by no means content with this discussion; and least of all, with my own part in it. This discontent affected me for some days, during which I wrote to Faraday, giving him no details, but expressing, in a general way, my dissatisfaction. I give the following extract from his reply:

Sydenham, Oct. 6, 1855.

My Dear Tyndall—These great meetings, of which I think very well altogether, advance science chiefly by bringing scientific men together and making them to know and be friends with each other; and I am sorry when that is not the effect in every part of their course. I know nothing except from what you tell me, for I have not yet looked at the reports of the proceedings; but let me, as an old man, who ought by this time to have profited by experience, say that when I was younger I found I often misinterpreted the intentions of people, and found they did not mean what at the time I supposed they meant; and, further, that as a general rule, it was better to be a little dull of apprehension where phrases seemed to imply pique, and quick in perception when, on the contrary, they seemed to imply kindly feeling. The real truth never fails ultimately to appear; and opposing parties, if wrong, are sooner convinced when replied to forbearingly, than when overwhelmed. All I mean to say is, that it is better to be blind to the results of partisanship, and quick to see good will. One has more happiness in one-self in endeavoring to follow the things that make for peace. You can hardly imagine how often I have been heated in private when opposed, as I have thought, un-justly and superciliously, and yet I have striven, and succeeded, I hope, in keeping down replies of the like kind. And I know I have never lost by it. I would not say all this to you did I not esteem you as a true philosopher and friend.*

Yours, very truly,
M. FARADAY

---

* Faraday would have been rejoiced to learn that, during its last meeting at Dundee, the British Association illustrated in a striking manner the function which he here describes as its principal one. In my own case, a brotherly welcome was everywhere manifested. In fact, the differences of really honorable and sane men are never beyond healing.

Identity of Electricities;
First Researches on Electrochemistry

I HAVE ALREADY once used the word "discomfort" in reference to the occasional state of Faraday's mind when experimenting. It was to him a discomfort to reason upon data which admitted of doubt. He hated what he called "doubtful knowledge," and ever tended either to transfer it into the region of undoubtful knowledge, or of certain and definite ignorance. Pretense of all kinds, whether in life or in philosophy, was hateful to him. He wished to know the reality of our nescience as well as of our science. "Be one thing or the other," he seemed to say to an unproved hypothesis; "come out as a solid truth, or disappear as a convicted lie." After making the great discovery which I have attempted to describe, a doubt seemed to beset him as regards the identity of electricities. "Is it right," he seemed to ask, "to call this agency which I have discovered electricity at all? Are there perfectly conclusive grounds for believing that the electricity of the machine, the pile, the gymnotus and torpedo, magnetoelectricity and thermoelectricity, are merely different manifestations of one and the same agent?" [3] To answer this question to his own satisfaction he formally reviewed the knowledge of that day. He added to it new experiments of his own, and finally decided in favor of the "identity of electricities." His paper upon this subject was read before the Royal Society on January 10 and 17, 1833.

After he had proved to his own satisfaction the identity of electricities, he tried to compare them quantitatively together. The terms quantity and intensity, which Faraday constantly used, need a word of explanation here. He might charge a single Leyden jar by twenty turns of his machine, or he might charge a battery of ten jars by the same number of turns. The *quantity* in both cases would be sensibly the same, but the *intensity* of

The use of the Leyden jar as a device in which an electrical charge may be stored is mentioned briefly. A bottle of glass was covered both on the inside and on the outside with tinfoil for about three-fourths the distance to the bottle's top. Passing through a wooden cap was a metal rod with a metal ball at the top and a metal chain extending to the bottom of the jar. Exposed parts of the glass were varnished. When an electric charge was applied to the ball, the charge spread immediately to the metal interior, drawing unlike electric charges from the earth to the metal exterior. The effect was to hold the first charge within the bottle and make it possible for other charges of the same kind to be added also.

the single jar would be the greatest, for here the electricity would be less diffused. Faraday first satisfied himself that the needle of his galvanometer was caused to swing through the same arc by the same quantity of machine electricity, whether it was condensed in a small battery or diffused over a large one. Thus the electricity developed by thirty turns of his machine produced, under very variable conditions of battery surface, the same deflection. Hence he inferred the possibility of comparing, as regards quantity, electricities which differ greatly from each other in intensity.

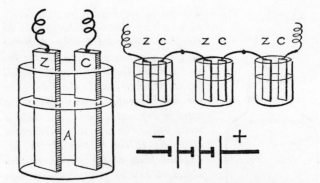

The voltaic cell referred to in this book was made from a piece of zinc (Z), a strip of copper (C) or platinum, and a jar containing some dilute sulphuric acid (A). When connection was made through an outside wire, a current flowed and the zinc was used up chemically. A group of cells arranged in a series formed a battery. The diagram for such a battery showed the zinc pieces as short, heavy blocks, the copper strips as long, thin lines. The electrical charges are negative for the zinc, positive for the copper.

His object now is to compare frictional with voltaic electricity. Moistening bibulous paper [4] with the iodide of potassium—a favorite test of his—and subjecting it to the action of machine electricity, he decomposed the iodide, and formed a brown spot where the iodine was liberated. Then he immersed two wires, one of zinc, the other of platinum, each $\frac{1}{13}$th of an inch in diameter, to a depth of $\frac{5}{8}$ths of an inch in acidulated water during eight beats of his watch, or $\frac{3}{20}$ths of a second;

and found that the needle of his galvanometer swung through the same arc, and colored his moistened paper to the same extent, as thirty turns of his large electrical machine. Twenty-eight turns of the machine produced an effect distinctly less than that produced by his two wires. Now, the quantity of water decomposed by the wires in this experiment totally eluded observation; it was immeasurably small; and still that amount of decomposition involved the development of a quantity of electric force which, if applied in a proper form, would kill a rat, and no man would like to bear it.

In his subsequent researches "on the absolute quantity of electricity associated with the particles of atoms of matter," he endeavors to give an idea of the amount of electrical force involved in the decomposition of a single grain of water. He is almost afraid to mention it, for he estimates it at 800,000 discharges of his large Leyden battery. This, if concentrated in a single discharge, would be equal to a very great flash of lightning; while the chemical action of a single grain of water on four grains of zinc would yield electricity equal in quantity to a powerful thunderstorm. Thus his mind rises from the minute to the vast, expanding involuntarily from the smallest laboratory fact till it embraces the largest and grandest natural phenomena.*

In reality, however, he is at this time only clearing his way, and he continues laboriously to clear it for some time afterwards. He is digging the shaft, guided by that instinct towards the mineral lode which was to him a rod of divination. *"Er riecht die Wahrheit,"* said the lamented Kohlrausch, an eminent German, once in my hearing; "He smells the truth." His eyes are now steadily fixed on this wonderful voltaic current, and he must learn more of its mode of transmission.

On May 23, 1833, he read a paper before the Royal Society "On a New Law of Electric Conduction." He found that, though the current passed through water, it did not pass through ice; why not, since they are one and the same substance? Some years subsequently he answered this

---

* Buff finds the quantity of electricity associated with one milligram of hydrogen in water to be equal to 45,480 charges of a Leyden jar, with a height of 480 millimeters, and a diameter of 160 millimeters. Weber and Kohlrausch have calculated that, if the quantity of electricity associated with one milligram of hydrogen in water were diffused over a cloud at a height of 1000 meters above the earth, it would exert upon an equal quantity of the opposite electricity at the earth's surface an attractive force of 2,268,000 kilograms. (*Electrolytische Maasbestimmungen,* 1856, page 262.)

question by saying that the liquid condition enables the molecule of water to turn round so as to
place itself in the proper line of polarization, while
the rigidity of the solid condition prevents this
arrangement. This polar arrangement must pre-
clude decomposition, and decomposition is an ac-
companiment of conduction. He then passed on to
other substances: to oxides and chlorides, and
iodides, and salts, and sulphurets,[5] and found them
all insulators when solid, and conductors when
fused. In all cases, moreover, except one—and
this exception he thought might be apparent only
—he found the passage of the current across the
fused compound to be accompanied by its decomposition. Is then the act of decomposition essential to the act of conduction in these bodies?
Even recently this question was warmly contested.
Faraday was very cautious latterly in expressing
himself upon this subject; but as a matter of fact
he held that an infinitesimal quantity of electricity
might pass through a compound liquid without
producing its decomposition. De la Rive, who has
been a great worker on the chemical phenomena
of the pile, is very emphatic on the other side.
Experiment, according to him and others, estab-
lishes in the most conclusive manner that no trace
of electricity can pass through a liquid compound

without producing its equivalent decomposition.*

Faraday has now got fairly entangled amid the chemical phenomena of the pile, and here his previous training under Davy must have been of the most important service to him. Why, he asks, should decomposition thus take place? What force is it that wrenches the locked constituents of these compounds asunder? On the 20th of June, 1833, he read a paper before the Royal Society "On Electrochemical Decomposition," in which he seeks to answer these questions. The notion had been entertained that the poles, as they are called, of the decomposing cell, or in other words the surfaces by which the current enters and quits the liquid, exercised electric attractions upon the constituents of the liquid and tore them asunder. Faraday combats this notion with extreme vigor. Litmus reveals, as you know, the action of an acid by turning red, turmeric reveals the action of an alkali by turning brown. Sulphate of soda, you know, is a salt compounded of the alkali soda and sulphuric acid. The voltaic current passing through a solution of this salt so decomposes it, that sulphuric acid appears at one pole of the decomposing cell and alkali at the other. Faraday

---

* *Faraday, sa Vie et ses Travaux,* page 20.

steeped a piece of litmus paper and a piece of turmeric paper in a solution of sulphate of soda; placing each of them upon a separate plate of glass, he connected them together by means of a string moistened with the same solution. He then attached one of them to the positive conductor of an electric machine, and the other to the gas pipes of this building. These he called his "discharging train." On turning the machine the electricity passed from paper to paper through the string, which might be varied in length from a few inches to seventy feet without changing the result. The first paper was reddened, declaring the presence of sulphuric acid; the second was browned, declaring the presence of the alkali soda. The dissolved salt, therefore, arranged in this fashion, was decomposed by the machine, exactly as it would have been by the voltaic current. When instead of using the positive conductor he used the negative, the positions of the acid and alkali were reversed. Thus he satisfied himself that chemical decomposition by the machine is obedient to the laws which rule decomposition by the pile.

And now he gradually abolishes those so-called poles, to the attraction of which electric decomposition had been ascribed. He connected a piece of turmeric paper moistened with the sulphate of

soda with the positive conductor of his machine;
then he placed a metallic point in connection with
his discharging train opposite the moist paper, so
that the electricity should discharge through the
air towards the point. The turning of the machine
caused the corners of the piece of turmeric paper
opposite the point to turn brown, thus declaring
the presence of alkali. He changed the turmeric
for litmus paper, and placed it, not in connection
with his conductor, but with his discharging train,
a metallic point connected with the conductor
being fixed at a couple of inches from the paper;
on turning the machine, acid was liberated at the
edges and corners of the litmus. He then placed
a series of pointed pieces of paper, each separate
piece being composed of two halves, one of litmus
and the other of turmeric paper, and all moistened
with sulphate of soda, in the line of the current
from the machine. The pieces of paper were separated from each other by spaces of air. The machine was turned; and it was always found that
at the point where the electricity entered the
paper, litmus was reddened, and at the point where
it quitted the paper, turmeric was browned.
"Here," he urges, "the poles are entirely abandoned, but we have still electrochemical decomposition." It is evident to him that instead of being

attracted by the poles, the bodies separated are *ejected* by the current. The effects thus obtained with poles of air he also succeeded in obtaining with poles of water. The advance in Faraday's own ideas made at this time is indicated by the word "ejected." He afterwards reiterates this view: the evolved substances are *expelled* from the decomposing body, and *not drawn out by an attraction.*

Having abolished this idea of polar attraction, he proceeds to enunciate and develop a theory of his own. He refers to Davy's celebrated Bakerian Lecture, given in 1806, which he says "is almost entirely occupied in the consideration of electrochemical decompositions." The facts recorded in that lecture Faraday regards as of the utmost value. But "the mode of action by which the effects take place is stated very generally; so generally, indeed, that probably a dozen precise schemes of electrochemical action might be drawn up, differing essentially from each other, yet all agreeing with the statement there given."

It appears to me that these words might with justice be applied to Faraday's own researches at this time. They furnish us with results of permanent value; but little help can be found in the theory advanced to account for them. It would, perhaps, be more correct to say that the theory itself is hardly presentable in any tangible form to the intellect. Faraday looks, and rightly looks, into the heart of the decomposing body itself; he sees, and rightly sees, active within it the forces which produce the decomposition, and he rejects, and rightly rejects, the notion of external attraction; but beyond the hypothesis of decompositions and recompositions, enunciated and developed by Grothuss and Davy, he does not, I think, help us to any definite conception as to how the force reaches the decomposing mass and acts within it. Nor, indeed, can this be done, until we know the true physical process which underlies what we call an electric current.

Faraday conceives of that current as "*an axis of power having contrary forces exactly equal in amount in opposite directions*"; but this definition, though much quoted and circulated, teaches us nothing regarding the current. An "axis" here can only mean a direction; and what we want to be able to conceive of is, not the axis along which the power acts, but the nature and mode of action of the power itself. He objects to the vagueness of De la Rive; but the fact is, that both he and De la Rive labor under the same difficulty. Neither wishes to commit himself to the notion of a current compounded of two electricities flowing in two opposite directions; but the time had not come, nor is it yet come,[6] for the displacement of this provisional fiction by the true mechanical conception. Still, however indistinct the theoretic notions of Faraday at this time may be, the facts which are rising before him and around him are leading him gradually, but surely, to results of incalculable importance in relation to the philosophy of the voltaic pile.

He had always some great object of research in view, but in the pursuit of it he frequently alighted on facts of collateral interest, to examine which he sometimes turned aside from his direct course. Thus we find the series of his researches on electrochemical decomposition interrupted by an inquiry into "the power of metals and other solids, to induce the combination of gaseous bodies." This inquiry, which was received by the Royal Society on November 30, 1833, though not so important as those which precede and follow it, illustrates throughout his strength as an experimenter. The power of spongy platinum to cause the combination of oxygen and hydrogen had been discovered by Döbereiner in 1823, and had been applied by him in the construction of his well-known philosophic lamp. It was shown subsequently by Dulong and Thenard that even a platinum wire, when perfectly cleansed, may be raised to incandescence by its action on a jet of cold hydrogen.

In his experiments on the decomposition of water, Faraday found that the positive platinum plate of the decomposing cell possessed in an extraordinary degree the power of causing oxygen and hydrogen to combine. He traced the cause of this to the perfect cleanness of the positive plate. Against it was liberated oxygen, which, with the powerful affinity of the "nascent state," swept away all impurity from the surface against which it was liberated. The bubbles of gas liberated on one of the platinum plates or wires of a decomposing cell are always much smaller, and they rise in much more rapid succession than those from the other. Knowing that oxygen is sixteen times heavier than hydrogen, I have more than once concluded, and, I fear, led others into the error of concluding, that the smaller and more quickly rising bubbles must belong to the lighter gas. The thing appeared so obvious that I did not give myself the trouble of looking at the battery, which would at once have told me the nature of the gas. But Faraday would never have been satisfied with a deduction if he could have reduced it to a fact. And he has taught me that the fact here is the direct reverse of what I supposed it to be. The small bubbles are oxygen, and their smallness is due to the perfect cleanness of the surface on which they are liberated. The hydrogen adhering to the other electrode swells into large bubbles, which rise in much slower succession; but when the current is reversed, the hydrogen is liberated upon the cleansed wire, and then its bubbles also become small.

Laws of Electrochemical Decomposition

In our conceptions and reasonings regarding the forces of nature, we perpetually make use of symbols which, when they possess a high representative value, we dignify with the name of theories. Thus, prompted by certain analogies, we ascribe electrical phenomena to the action of a peculiar fluid, sometimes flowing, sometimes at rest. Such conceptions have their advantages and their disadvantages; they afford peaceful lodging to the intellect for a time, but they also circumscribe it, and by and by, when the mind has grown too large for its lodging, it often finds difficulty in breaking down the walls of what has become its prison instead of its home.*

* I copy these words from the printed abstract of a Friday evening lecture, given by myself, because they remind me of Faraday's voice, responding to the utterance by an emphatic "hear! hear!"—*Proceedings of the Royal Institution*, volume 2, page 132.

No man ever felt this tyranny of symbols more deeply than Faraday, and no man was ever more assiduous than he to liberate himself from them, and the terms which suggested them. Calling Dr. Whewell to his aid in 1833, he endeavored to displace by others all terms tainted by a foregone conclusion. His paper on electrochemical decomposition, received by the Royal Society on January 9, 1834, opens with the proposal of a new terminology. He would avoid the word "current" if he could.* He does abandon the word "poles" as applied to the ends of a decomposing cell, because it suggests the idea of attraction, substituting for it the perfectly natural term *electrodes*. He applied the term *electrolyte* to every substance which can be decomposed by the current, and the act of decomposition he called *electrolysis*. All these terms have become current in science. He called the positive electrode the *anode*, and the negative one the *cathode*, but these terms, though frequently used, have not enjoyed the same currency as the others. The terms *anion* and *cation*,

---

* In 1838 he expresses himself thus: "The word current is so expressive in common language that when applied in the consideration of electrical phenomena, we can hardly divest it sufficiently of its meaning, or prevent our minds from being prejudiced by it." (*Experimental Researches*, volume 1, page 515.)

which he applied to the constituents of the decomposed electrolyte, and the term *ion,* which included both anions and cations, are still less frequently employed.

Faraday now passes from terminology to research; he sees the necessity of quantitative determinations, and seeks to supply himself with a measure of voltaic electricity. This he finds in the quantity of water decomposed by the current. He tests this measure in all possible ways, to assure himself that no error can arise from its employment. He places in the course of one and the same current a series of cells with electrodes of different sizes, some of them plates of platinum, others merely platinum wires, and collects the gas liberated on each distinct pair of electrodes. He finds the quantity of gas to be the same for all. Thus he concludes that when the same quantity of electricity is caused to pass through a series of cells containing acidulated water, the electrochemical action is independent of the size of the electrodes.* He next proves that variations in intensity do not interfere with this equality of action. Whether his battery is charged with strong acid or with weak; whether it consists of five pairs or of

---

* This conclusion needs qualification. Faraday overlooked the part played by ozone.

fifty pairs; in short, whatever be its source, when the same current is sent through his series of cells the same amount of decomposition takes place in all. He next assures himself that the strength or weakness of his dilute acid does not interfere with this law. Sending the same current through a series of cells containing mixtures of sulphuric acid and water of different strengths, he finds, however the proportion of acid to water might vary, the same amount of gas to be collected in all the cells. A crowd of facts of this character forced upon Faraday's mind the conclusion that the amount of electrochemical decomposition depends, not upon the size of the electrodes, not upon the intensity of the current, not upon the strength of the solution, but solely upon the quantity of electricity which passes through the cell. The quantity of electricity, he concludes, is proportional to the amount of chemical action. On this law Faraday based the construction of his celebrated voltameter, or measure of voltaic electricity.

But before he can apply this measure he must clear his ground of numerous possible sources of error. The decomposition of his acidulated water is certainly a *direct* result of the current; but as the varied and important researches of Messrs. Becquerel, De la Rive, and others had shown, there are also *secondary* actions which may materially interfere with and complicate the pure action of the current. These actions may occur in two ways: either the liberated *ion* may seize upon the electrode against which it is set free, forming a chemical compound with that electrode; or it may seize upon the substance of the electrolyte itself, and thus introduce into the circuit chemical actions over and above those due to the current. Faraday subjected these secondary actions to an exhaustive examination. Instructed by his experiments, and rendered competent by them to distinguish between primary and secondary results, he proceeds to establish the doctrine of "definite electrochemical decomposition."

Into the same circuit he introduced his voltameter, which consisted of a graduated tube filled with acidulated water and provided with platinum plates for the decomposition of the water, and also a cell containing chloride of tin. Experiments already referred to had taught him that this substance, though an insulator when solid, is a conductor when fused, the passage of the current being always accompanied by the decomposition of the chloride. He wished to ascertain what relation this decomposition bore to that of the water in his voltameter.

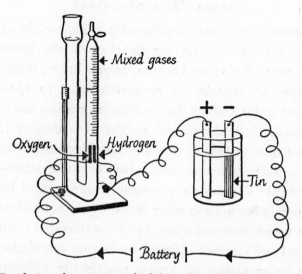

Faraday's voltameter, at the left, and a chloride of tin cell, at the right, are shown as arranged for measuring the quantity of electricity flowing through battery wires in a certain length of time. In the voltameter, acidulated water was decomposed into oxygen, at the left-hand platinum plate, and hydrogen, at the right-hand platinum plate. The gas bubbles rose together and the combined volume was measured from the tube markings. In the connected cell, metallic tin was deposited at the negative plate, the quantity of the tin being determined by weighing. Faraday found a definite relation between the volume of the gases and the weight of the tin formed.

Completing his circuit, he permitted the current to continue until "a reasonable quantity of gas" was collected in the voltameter. The circuit was then broken, and the quantity of tin liberated compared with the quantity of gas. The weight of the former was 3.2 grains, that of the latter 0.49742 of a grain. Oxygen, as you know, unites with hydrogen in the proportion of 8 to 1, to form water. Calling the equivalent, or as it is sometimes called, the atomic weight of hydrogen 1, that of oxygen is 8; that of water is consequently 8 + 1 or 9.[7] Now if the quantity of water decomposed in Faraday's experiment be represented by the number 9, or in other words by the equivalent of water, then the quantity of tin liberated from the fused chloride is found by an easy calculation to be 57.9, which is almost exactly the chemical equivalent of tin. Thus both the water and the chloride were broken up in proportions expressed by their respective equivalents. The amount of electric force which wrenched asunder the constituents of the molecule of water was competent, and neither more nor less than competent, to wrench asunder the constituents of the molecules of the chloride of tin. The fact is typical. With the indications of his voltameter he compared the decompositions of other substances, both singly and in series. He submitted his conclusions to numberless tests. He purposely introduced secondary actions. He endeavored to hamper the fulfilment of those laws which it was the intense desire of his mind to see established. But from all these difficulties emerged the golden truth, that under every variety of circumstances the decompositions of the voltaic current are as definite in their character as those chemical combinations which gave birth to the atomic theory. This law of electrochemical decomposition ranks, in point of importance, with that of definite combining proportions in chemistry.

Origin of Power in the Voltaic Pile

IN ONE of the public areas of the town of Como stands a statue with no inscription on its pedestal, save that of a single name, "Volta." The bearer of that name occupies a place for ever memorable in the history of science. To him we owe the discovery of the voltaic pile, to which for a brief interval we must now turn our attention.

The objects of scientific thought being the passionless laws and phenomena of external nature, one might suppose that their investigation and discussion would be completely withdrawn from the region of the feelings, and pursued by the cold dry light of the intellect alone. This, however, is not always the case. Man carries his heart with

him into all his works. You cannot separate the
moral and emotional from the intellectual; and
thus it is that the discussion of a point of science
may rise to the heat of a battlefield. The fight
between the rival optical theories of emission and
undulation [8] was of this fierce character; and
scarcely less fierce for many years was the contest
as to the origin and maintenance of the power of
the voltaic pile. Volta himself supposed it to reside
in the contact of different metals. Here was exerted his "electromotive force," which tore the
combined electricities asunder and drove them as
currents in opposite directions. To render the cir-
culation of the current possible, it was necessary to
connect the metals by a moist conductor; for when
any two metals were connected by a third, their relation to each other was such that a complete neu-
tralization of the electric motion was the result.
Volta's theory of metallic contact was so clear, so
beautiful, and apparently so complete, that the
best intellects of Europe accepted it as the expression of natural law.

Volta himself knew nothing of the chemical
phenomena of the pile; but as soon as these became known, suggestions and intimations appeared that chemical action, and not metallic contact, might be the real source of voltaic electricity.

This idea was expressed by Fabroni in Italy, and by Wollaston in England. It was developed and maintained by those "admirable electricians," Becquerel, of Paris, and De la Rive, of Geneva. The contact theory, on the other hand, received its chief development and illustration in Germany. It was long the scientific creed of the great chemists and natural philosophers of that country, and to the present hour there may be some of them unable to liberate themselves from the fascination of their first love.

After the researches which I have endeavored to place before you, it was impossible for Faraday to avoid taking a side in this controversy. He did so in a paper "On the Electricity of the Voltaic Pile," received by the Royal Society on the 7th of April, 1834. His position in the controversy might have been predicted. He saw chemical effects going hand in hand with electrical effects, the one being proportional to the other; and, in the paper now before us, he proved that when the former were excluded, the latter were sought for in vain. He produced a current without metallic contact; he discovered liquids which, though competent to transmit the feeblest currents—competent therefore to allow the electricity of contact to flow through them if it were able to form a current—

were absolutely powerless when chemically in-
active.

One of the very few experimental mistakes
of Faraday occurred in this investigation. He
thought that with a single voltaic cell he had obtained the spark *before the metals touched,* but
he subsequently discovered his error. To enable
the voltaic spark to pass through air before the
terminals of the battery were united, it was necessary to exalt the electromotive force of the battery
by multiplying its elements; but all the elements
Faraday possessed were unequal to the task of urg-
ing the spark across the shortest measurable space
of air. Nor, indeed, could the action of the battery,
the different metals of which were in contact with
each other, decide the point in question. Still, as
regards the identity of electricities from various
sources, it was at that day of great importance to
determine whether or not the voltaic current
could jump, as a spark, across an interval before
contact. Faraday's friend, Mr. Gassiot, solved this
problem. He erected a battery of 4000 cells, and
with it urged a stream of sparks from terminal to
terminal, when separated from each other by a
measurable space of air.

The memoir on the "electricity of the voltaic
pile," published in 1834, appears to have produced

but little impression upon the supporters of the contact theory. These indeed were men of too great intellectual weight and insight lightly to take up, or lightly to abandon, a theory. Faraday therefore resumed the attack in a paper, communicated to the Royal Society on the 6th of February, 1840. In this paper he hampered his antagonists by a crowd of adverse experiments. He hung difficulty after difficulty about the neck of the contact theory, until in its efforts to escape from his assaults it so changed its character as to become a thing totally different from the theory proposed by Volta. The more persistently it was defended, however, the more clearly did it show itself to be a congeries of devices, bearing the stamp of dialectic skill rather than of natural truth.

In conclusion, Faraday brought to bear upon it an argument which, had its full weight and purport been understood at the time, would have instantly decided the controversy. "The contact theory," he urged, "assumed that a force which is able to overcome powerful resistance, as for instance that of the conductors, good or bad, through which the current passes, and that again of the electrolytic action where bodies are decomposed by it, *can arise out of nothing;* that, without any change in the acting matter, or the consumption of any generating force, a current shall be produced which shall go on for ever against a constant resistance, or only be stopped, as in the voltaic trough, by the ruins which its exertion has heaped up in its own course. This would indeed be *a creation of power*, and is like no other force in nature. We have many processes by which the *form* of the power may be so changed, that an apparent *conversion* of one into the other takes place. So we can change chemical force into the electric current, or the current into chemical force. The beautiful experiments of Seebeck and Peltier show the convertibility of heat and electricity; and others by Oersted and myself show the convertibility of electricity and magnetism. *But in no case, not even in those of the gymnotus and torpedo, is there a pure creation or a production of power without a corresponding exhaustion of something to supply it.*"

These words were published more than two years before either Mayer printed his brief but celebrated essay on the forces of inorganic nature, or Mr. Joule published his first famous experiments on the mechanical value of heat. They illustrate the fact that before any great scientific principle receives distinct enunciation by individuals, it dwells more or less clearly in the general scientific mind. The intellectual plateau is already high, and our discoverers are those who, like peaks above the plateau, rise a little above the general level of thought at the time.

But many years prior even to the foregoing utterance of Faraday, a similar argument had been employed. I quote here with equal pleasure and admiration the following passage written by Dr. Roget so far back as 1829. Speaking of the contact theory, he says: "If there could exist a power having the property ascribed to it by the hypothesis, namely, that of giving continual impulse to a fluid in one constant direction, without being exhausted by its own action, it would differ essentially from all the known powers in nature. All the powers and sources of motion with the operation of which we are acquainted, when producing these peculiar effects, *are expended in the same proportion as those effects are produced; and hence arises the impossibility of obtaining by their agency a perpetual effect; or in other words a perpetual motion.* But the electromotive force, ascribed by Volta to the metals when in contact, is a force which, as long as a free course is allowed to the electricity it sets in motion, is never expended, and continues to be excited with undiminished power in the production of a never-ceasing effect. Against the truth of such a supposition the probabilities are all but infinite." When this argument, which he employed independently, had clearly fixed itself in his mind, Faraday never cared to experiment further on the source of electricity in the voltaic pile. The argument appeared to him "to remove *the foundation itself* of the contact theory," and he afterwards let it crumble down in peace.*

---

* To account for the *electric current*, which was really the core of the whole discussion, Faraday demonstrated the impotence of the contact theory as then enunciated and defended. Still, it is certain that two different metals, when brought into contact, charge themselves, the one with positive and the other with negative electricity. I had the pleasure of going over this ground with Kohlrausch in 1849, and his experiments left no doubt upon my mind that the contact electricity of Volta was a reality, though it could produce no current. With one of the beautiful instruments devised by himself, Sir William Thomson has rendered this point capable of sure and easy demonstration; and he and others now hold what may be called a contact theory, which, while it takes into account the action of the metals, also embraces the chemical phenomena of the circuit. Helmholtz, I believe, was the first to give the contact theory this new form, in his celebrated essay, *Ueber die Erhaltung der Kraft*, page 45.

Researches on Frictional Electricity; Induction; Conduction; Specific Inductive Capacity; Theory of Contiguous Particles

THE BURST of power which had filled the four preceding years with an amount of experimental work unparalleled in the history of science partially subsided in 1835, and the only scientific paper contributed by Faraday in that year was a comparatively unimportant one, "On an Improved Form of the Voltaic Battery." He brooded for a time; his experiments on electrolysis had long filled his mind; he looked, as already stated, into the very heart of the electrolyte, endeavoring to render the play of its atoms visible to his mental eye. He had no doubt that in this case what is called "the electric current" was propagated from particle to particle of the electrolyte; he accepted the doctrine of decomposition and recomposition which, according to Grothuss and Davy, ran from electrode to electrode. And the thought impressed him more and more that ordinary electric induction was also transmitted and sustained by the action of *"contiguous particles."* [9]

His first great paper on frictional electricity was sent to the Royal Society on November 30, 1837. We here find him face to face with an idea which beset his mind throughout his whole subsequent life, the idea of *action at a distance*. It perplexed and bewildered him. In his attempts to get rid of this perplexity, he was often unconsciously rebelling against the limitations of the intellect itself. He loved to quote Newton upon this point; over and over again he introduces his memorable words, "That gravity should be innate, inherent, and essential to matter, so that one body may act upon another at a distance through a *vacuum* and without the mediation of anything else, by and through which this action and force may be conveyed from one to another, is to me so great an absurdity, that I believe no man who has in philosophical matters a competent faculty of thinking can ever fall into it. Gravity must be caused by an agent acting constantly according to certain laws; but whether this agent be material or immaterial, I have left to the consideration of my readers." *

Faraday does not see the same difficulty in his contiguous particles. And yet, by transferring the conception from masses to particles, we simply lessen size and distance, but we do not alter the quality of the conception. Whatever difficulty the mind experiences in conceiving of action at sensible distances, besets it also when it attempts to conceive of action at insensible distances. Still the investigation of the point whether electric and magnetic effects were wrought out through the intervention of contiguous particles or not, had a physical interest altogether apart from the metaphysical difficulty. Faraday grapples with the subject experimentally. By simple intuition he sees that action at a distance must be exerted in straight lines. Gravity, he knows, will not turn a corner, but exerts its pull along a right line; hence his aim and effort to ascertain whether electric action ever takes place in curved lines. This once proved, it would follow that the action is carried on *by means of a medium* surrounding the electrified bodies. His experiments in 1837 reduced, in his opinion, this point of demonstration. He then found that he could electrify, by induction,

---

* Newton's third letter to Bentley.

an insulated sphere placed completely in the shadow of a body which screened it from direct action. He pictured the lines of electric force bending round the edges of the screen, and re-uniting on the other side of it; and he proved that in many cases the augmentation of the distance between his insulated sphere and the inducing body, instead of lessening, increased the charge of the sphere. This he ascribed to the coalescence of the lines of electric force at some distance behind the screen.

Faraday's theoretic views on this subject have not received general acceptance, but they drove him to experiment, and experiment with him was always prolific of results. By suitable arrangements he placed a metallic sphere in the middle of a large hollow sphere, leaving a space of something more than half an inch between them. The interior sphere was insulated, the external one uninsulated. To the former he communicated a definite charge of electricity. It acted by induction upon the con-cave surface of the latter, and he examined how this act of induction was effected by placing in-sulators of various kinds between the two spheres. He tried gases, liquids, and solids, but the solids alone gave him positive results. He constructed two instruments of the foregoing description,

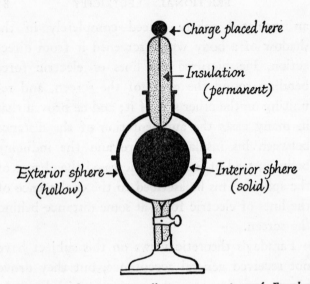

The figure shows a partially cutaway view of Faraday's sphere-within-a-sphere apparatus in which air was the insulator. A charge applied to the metal knob would spread instantly to the inner sphere. An opposite charge would be drawn from the earth to the outer cylinder. The amount of the induced charge would be measured.

equal in size and similar in form. The interior sphere of each communicated with the external air by a brass stem ending in a knob. The apparatus was virtually a Leyden jar, the two coatings of which were the two spheres, with a thick and variable insulator between them. The amount of charge in each jar was determined by bringing a proof plane into contact with its knob and meas-

uring by a torsion balance the charge taken away.
He first charged one of his instruments, and then
dividing the charge with the other, found that
when air intervened in both cases the charge was
equally divided. But when shellac, sulphur, or
spermaceti was interposed between the two
spheres of one jar, while air occupied this interval
in the other, then he found that the instrument
occupied by the "solid dielectric" takes *more than
half* the original charge. A portion of the charge
was absorbed by the dielectric itself. The electricity took time to penetrate the dielectric. Immediately after the discharge of the apparatus, no
trace of electricity was found upon its knob. But
after a time electricity was found there, the charge
having gradually returned from the dielectric in
which it had been lodged. Different insulators
possess this power of permitting the charge to enter
them in different degrees. Faraday figured their
particles as polarized, and he concluded that the
force of induction is propagated from particle to
particle of the dielectric from the inner sphere to
the outer one. This power of propagation possessed by insulators he called their "specific inductive capacity."

Faraday visualizes with the utmost clearness the
state of his contiguous particles; one after another

they become charged, each succeeding particle depending for its charge upon its predecessor. And now he seeks to break down the wall of partition between conductors and insulators. "Can we not," he says, "by a gradual chain of association carry up discharge from its occurrence in air through spermaceti and water, to solutions, and then on to chlorides, oxides, and metals, without any essential change in its character?" Even copper, he urges, offers a resistance to the transmission of electricity. The action of its particles differs from those of an insulator only in degree. They are charged like the particles of the insulator, but they discharge with greater ease and rapidity; and this rapidity of molecular discharge is what we call conduction. Conduction, then, is always preceded by atomic induction; and when, through some quality of the body which Faraday does not define, the atomic discharge is rendered slow and difficult, conduction passes into insulation.

Though they are often obscure, a fine vein of philosophic thought runs through those investigations. The mind of the philosopher dwells amid those agencies which underlie the visible phenomena of induction and conduction; and he tries by the strong light of his imagination to see the very molecules of his dielectrics. It would, however, be easy to criticize these researches, easy to show the looseness, and sometimes the inaccuracy, of the phraseology employed; but this critical spirit will get little good out of Faraday. Rather let those who ponder his works seek to realize the object he set before him, not permitting his occasional vagueness to interfere with their appreciation of his speculations. We may see the ripples and eddies and vortices of a flowing stream without being able to resolve all these motions into their constituent elements; and so it sometimes strikes me that Faraday clearly saw the play of fluids and ethers and atoms, though his previous training did not enable him to resolve what he saw into its constituents, or describe it in a manner satisfactory to a mind versed in mechanics. And then again occur, I confess, dark sayings, difficult to be understood, which disturb my confidence in this conclusion. It must, however, always be remembered that he works at the very boundaries of our knowledge, and that his mind habitually dwells in the "boundless contiguity of shade" by which that knowledge is surrounded.

In the researches now under review the ratio of speculation and reasoning to experiment is far higher than in any of Faraday's previous works. Amid much that is entangled and dark we have flashes of wondrous insight and utterances which seem less the product of reasoning than of revelation. I will confine myself here to one example of this divining power. By his most ingenious device of a rapidly rotating mirror, Wheatstone had proved that electricity required time to pass through a wire, the current reaching the middle of the wire later than its two ends. "If," says Faraday, "the two ends of the wire in Professor Wheatstone's experiments were immediately connected with two large insulated metallic surfaces exposed to the air, so that the primary act of induction, after making the contact for discharge, might be in part removed from the internal portion of the wire at the first instance, and disposed for the moment on its surface jointly with the air and surrounding conductors, then I venture to anticipate that the middle spark would be more retarded than before. And if those two plates were the inner and outer coatings of a large jar or Leyden battery, then the retardation of the spark would be much greater." This was only a *prediction*, for the experiment was not made.* Sixteen

---

* Had Sir Charles Wheatstone been induced to resume his measurements, varying the substances through which, and the conditions under which, the current is propagated, he might have rendered great service to science, both theoretic and experimental.

years subsequently, however, the proper conditions came into play, and Faraday was able to show that the observations of Werner Siemens and Latimer Clark on subterraneous and submarine wires were illustrations, on a grand scale, of the principle which he had enunciated in 1838. The wires and the surrounding water act as a Leyden jar, and the retardation of the current predicted by Faraday manifests itself in every message sent by such cables.

The meaning of Faraday in these memoirs on induction and conduction is, as I have said, by no means always clear; and the difficulty will be most felt by those who are best trained in ordinary theoretic conceptions. He does not know the reader's needs, and he therefore does not meet them. For instance he speaks over and over again of the impossibility of charging a body with one electricity, though the impossibility is by no means evident. The key to the difficulty is this. He looks upon every insulated conductor as the inner coating of a Leyden jar. An insulated sphere in the middle of a room is to his mind such a coating; the walls are the outer coating, while the air between both is the insulator, across which the charge acts by induction. Without this reaction of the walls upon the sphere you could no more, according to Faraday, charge it with electricity than you could charge a Leyden jar, if its outer coating were removed. Distance with him is immaterial. His strength as a generalizer enables him to dissolve the idea of magnitude; and if you abolish the walls of the room—even the earth itself—he would make the sun and planets the outer coating of his jar. I dare not contend that Faraday in these memoirs made all his theoretic positions good. But a pure vein of philosophy runs through these writings; while his experiments and reasonings on the forms and phenomena of electrical discharge are of imperishable importance.

Rest Needed—Visit to Switzerland

THE LAST of these memoirs was dated from the Royal Institution in June, 1838. It concludes the first volume of his *Experimental Researches on Electricity*. In 1840, as already stated, he made his final assault on the contact theory, from which it never recovered.* He was now feeling the effects of the mental strain to which he had been subjected for so many years. During these years he repeatedly broke down. His wife alone witnessed the extent of his prostration, and to her loving care we, and the world, are indebted for the enjoyment of his presence here so long. He found occasional relief in a theater. He frequently quitted London and went to Brighton and else-

---

* See note, page 79.

where, always choosing a situation which commanded a view of the sea, or of some other pleasant horizon, where he could sit and gaze and feel the gradual revival of the faith that

> *"Nature never did betray*
> *The heart that loved her."*

But very often for some days after his removal to the country, he would be unable to do more than sit at a window and look out upon the sea and sky.

In 1841, his state became more serious than it had ever been before. A published letter to Mr. Richard Taylor, dated March 11, 1843, contains an allusion to his previous condition. "You are aware," he says, "that considerations regarding health have prevented me from working or reading on science for the last two years." This, at one period or another of their lives, seems to be the fate of most great investigators. They do not know the limits of the constitutional strength until they have transgressed them. It is, perhaps, right that they should transgress them, in order to ascertain where they lie. Faraday, however, though he went far towards it, did not push his transgression beyond his power of restitution. In 1841 Mrs. Faraday and he went to Switzerland, under the affectionate charge of her brother, Mr. George Barnard, the artist. This time of suffering throws fresh light upon his character. I have said that sweetness and gentleness were not its only constituents; that he was also fiery and strong. At the time now referred to, his fire was low and his strength distilled away; but the residue of his life was neither irritability nor discontent. He was unfit to mingle in society, for conversation was a pain to him; but let us observe the great man-child when alone. He is at the village of Interlaken, enjoying Jungfrau sunsets, and at times watching the Swiss nailers making their nails. He keeps a little journal, in which he describes the process of nailmaking, and incidentally throws a luminous beam upon himself.

"*August* 2, 1841—Clout nailmaking goes on here rather considerably, and is a very neat and pretty operation to observe. I love a smith's shop and anything relating to smithery. *My father was a smith.*"

From Interlaken he went to the falls of the Giessbach, on the pleasant lake of Brientz. And here we have him watching the shoot of the cataract down its series of precipices. It is shattered into foam at the base of each, and tossed by its own recoil as water dust through the air. The sun is at his back, shining on the drifting spray, and he thus describes and muses on what he sees:

"*August* 12, 1841—Today every fall was foaming from the abundance of water, and the current of wind brought down by it was in some places too strong to stand against. The sun shone brightly, and the rainbows seen from various points were very beautiful. One at the bottom of a fine but furious fall was very pleasant—there it remained motionless, whilst the gusts and clouds of spray swept furiously across its place and were dashed against the rock. It looked like a spirit strong in faith and steadfast in the midst of the storm of passions sweeping across it, and though it might fade and revive, still it held on to the rock as in hope and giving hope. And the very drops, which in the whirlwind of their fury seemed as if they would carry all away, were made to revive it and give it greater beauty."

Magnetization of Light

Bᴜᴛ ᴡᴇ must quit the man and go on to the discoverer: we shall return for a brief space to his company by and by. Carry your thoughts back to his last experiments, and see him endeavoring to prove that induction is due to the action of contiguous particles. He knew that polarized light was a most subtle and delicate investigator of molecular condition. He used it in 1834 in exploring his electrolytes, and he tried it in 1838 upon his dielectrics. At that time he coated two opposite faces of a glass cube with tinfoil, connected one coating with his powerful electric machine and the other with the earth, and examined by polarized light the condition of the glass when thus subjected to strong electric influence. He failed to obtain any effect; still he was persuaded an action existed, and required only suitable means to call it forth.

After his return from Switzerland he was beset by these thoughts. They were more inspired than logical; but he resorted to magnets and proved his inspiration true. His dislike of "doubtful knowledge" and his efforts to liberate his mind from the thraldom of hypotheses have been already referred to. Still this rebel against theory was incessantly theorizing himself. His principal researches are all connected by an undercurrent of speculation. Theoretic ideas were the very sap of his intellect—the source from which all his strength as an experimenter was derived. While once sauntering with him through the Crystal Palace at Sydenham, I asked him what directed his attention to the magnetization of light. It was his theoretic notions. He had certain views regarding the unity and convertibility of natural forces; certain ideas regarding the vibrations of light and their relations to the lines of magnetic force; these views and ideas drove him to investigation. And so it must always be: the great experimentalist must ever be the habitual theorist, whether or not he gives to his theories formal enunciation.

Faraday, you have been informed,[10] endeavored

to improve the manufacture of glass for optical purposes. But though he produced a heavy glass of great refractive power, its value to optics did not repay him for the pains and labor bestowed on it. Now, however, we reach a result established by means of this same heavy glass, which made ample amends for all.

In November, 1845, he announced his discovery of the "Magnetization of Light and the Illumination of the Lines of Magnetic Force." This title provoked comment at the time, and caused misapprehension. He therefore added an explanatory note; but the note left his meaning as entangled as before. In fact Faraday had notions regarding the magnetization of light which were peculiar to himself, and untranslatable into the scientific language of the time. Probably no other philosopher of his day would have employed the phrases just quoted as appropriate to the discovery announced in 1845. But Faraday was more than a philosopher; he was a prophet, and often wrought by an inspiration to be understood by sympathy alone. The prophetic element in his character occasionally colored, and even injured, the utterance of the man of science; but, subtracting that element, though you might have conferred on him intellectual symmetry, you would have destroyed his motive force.

But let us pass from the label of this casket to the jewel it contains. "I have long," he says, "held an opinion, almost amounting to conviction, in common, I believe, with many other lovers of natural knowledge, that the various forms under which the forces of matter are made manifest have one common origin; in other words, are so directly related and mutually dependent, that they are convertible, as it were, into one another, and possess equivalents of power in their action. . . . This strong persuasion," he adds, "extended to the powers of light." And then he examines the action of magnets upon light. From conversation with him and Anderson, I should infer that the labor preceding this discovery was very great. The world knows little of the toil of the discoverer. It sees the climber jubilant on the mountain top, but does not know the labor expended in reaching it. Probably hundreds of experiments had been made on transparent crystals before he thought of testing his heavy glass. Here is his own clear and simple description of the result of his first experiment with this substance: "A piece of this glass, about two inches square, and 0.5 of an inch thick, having flat and polished edges, was placed as a *diamagnetic* * between the poles (not as yet magnetized by the electric current), so that the polarized ray should pass through its length; the glass acted as air, water, or any other transparent substance would do; and if the eyepiece were previously turned into such a position that the polarized ray was extinguished, or rather the image produced by it rendered invisible, then the introduction of the glass made no alteration in this respect. In this state of circumstances, the force of the electromagnet was developed by sending an electric current through its coils, and immediately the image of the lamp flame became visible and continued so as long as the arrangement continued magnetic. On stopping the electric current, and so causing the magnetic force to cease, the light instantly disappeared. These phenomena could be renewed at pleasure, at any instant of time, and upon any occasion, showing a perfect dependence of cause and effect."

In a beam of ordinary light the particles of the luminiferous ether vibrate in all directions per-

---

* "By a *diamagnetic*," says Faraday, "I mean a body through which lines of magnetic force are passing, and which does not by their action assume the usual magnetic state of iron or loadstone." Faraday subsequently used this term in a different sense from that here given, as will immediately appear.

pendicular to the line of progression; by the act of polarization, performed here by Faraday, all oscillations but those parallel to a certain plane are eliminated. When the plane of vibration of the polarizer coincides with that of the analyzer, a portion of the beam passes through both; but when these two planes are at right angles to each other, the beam is extinguished. If by any means, while the polarizer and analyzer remain thus crossed, the plane of vibration of the polarized beam between them could be changed, then the light would be, in part at least, transmitted. In Faraday's experiment this was accomplished. His magnet turned the plane of polarization of the beam through a certain angle, and thus enabled it to get through the analyzer; so that "the magnetization of light and the illumination of the magnetic lines of force" becomes, when expressed in the language of modern theory, *the rotation of the plane of polarization.*

To him, as to all true philosophers, the main value of a fact was its position and suggestiveness in the general sequence of scientific truth. Hence, having established the existence of a phenomenon, his habit was to look at it from all possible points of view, and to develop its relationship to other phenomena. He proved that the direction of the

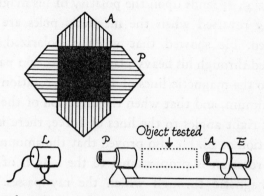

The *polarization equipment referred to makes use of the peculiar effect of the mineral tourmaline upon a ray of light. This substance is transparent but allows only that light to pass which is vibrating in a certain plane; the light in all other planes is stopped. That which passes is called polarized light.*

The polarized light from one sheet of tourmaline can pass through another sheet of it if the crystals are parallel. If the second is at a right angle to the other, as in the upper figure, the beam is extinguished.

Some transparent substances can rotate the plane of polarized light. The polarimeter tested these substances. As indicated in the lower figure, this device had a light source (L), a tourmaline piece to produce a polarized beam (P), an analyzer (A) carrying the second piece of tourmaline set into a rotating eyepiece (E). The object to be tested for its power of turning the plane of a polarized ray was placed between P and A. The eyepiece was then turned until the beam coming through was extinguished, the angle of turning being measured.

The use that Faraday made of the equipment is explained in the text.

rotation depends upon the polarity of his magnet; being reversed when the magnetic poles are reversed. He showed that when a polarized ray passed through his heavy glass in a direction parallel to the magnetic lines of force, the rotation is a maximum, and that when the direction of the ray is at right angles to the lines of force, there is no rotation at all. He also proved that the amount of the rotation is proportional to the length of the diamagnetic through which the ray passes. He operated with liquids and solutions. Of aqueous solutions he tried 150 and more, and found the power in all of them. He then examined gases; but here all his efforts to produce any sensible action upon the polarized beam were ineffectual. He then passed from magnets to currents, enclosing bars of heavy glass, and tubes containing liquids and aqueous solutions within an electromagnetic helix. A current sent through the helix caused the plane of polarization to rotate, and always *in the direction of the current*. The rotation was reversed when the current was reversed. In the case of magnets, he observed a gradual, though quick, ascent of the transmitted beam from a state of darkness to its maximum brilliancy, when the magnet was excited. In the case of currents, the beam attained *at once* its maximum. This he showed to be due to *the time* required by the iron of the electro-magnet to assume its full magnetic power, which time vanishes when a current, without iron, is employed. "In this experiment," he says, "we may, I think, justly say that a ray of light is electrified, and the electric forces illuminated." In the helix, as with the magnets, he submitted *air* to magnetic influence "carefully and anxiously," but could not discover any trace of action on the polarized ray.

Many substances possess the power of turning the plane of polarization without the intervention of magnetism. Oil of turpentine and quartz are examples; but Faraday showed that—while in one direction, that is, across the lines of magnetic force —his rotation is zero, augmenting gradually from this until it attains its maximum, when the direction of the ray is parallel to the lines of force; in the oil of turpentine the rotation is independent of the direction of the ray. But he showed that a still more profound distinction exists between the magnetic rotation and the natural one. I will try to explain how. Suppose a tube with glass ends containing oil of turpentine to be placed north and south. Fixing the eye at the south end of the tube, let a polarized beam be sent through it from the north. To the observer in this position the rotation of the plane of polarization, by the turpentine, is *right-handed*. Let the eye be placed at the north end of the tube, and a beam be sent through it from the south; the rotation is still right-handed. Not so, however, when a bar of heavy glass is subjected to the action of an electric current. In this case if, in the first position of the eye, the rotation be right-handed, in the second position it is left-handed. These considerations make it manifest that if a polarized beam, after having passed through the oil of turpentine in its natural state, could by any means be reflected back through the liquid, the rotation impressed upon the direct beam would be exactly neutralized by that impressed upon the reflected one. Not so with the induced magnetic effect. Here it is manifest that the rotation would be doubled by the act of reflection. Hence Faraday concludes that the particles of the oil of turpentine which rotate by virtue of their natural force, and those which rotate in virtue of the induced force, cannot be in the same condition. The same remark applies to all bodies which possess a natural power of rotating the plane of polarization.

And then he proceeded with exquisite skill and insight to take advantage of this conclusion. He silvered the ends of his piece of heavy glass, leaving, however, a narrow portion parallel to two edges diagonally opposed to each other unsilvered. He then sent his beam through this uncovered portion, and by suitably inclining his glass caused the beam within it to reach his eye first direct, and then after two, four, and six reflections. These corresponded to the passage of the ray once, three times, five times, and seven times through the glass. He thus established with numerical accuracy the exact proportionality of the rotation to the distance traversed by the polarized beam. Thus in one series of experiments where the rotation required by the direct beam was 12°, that acquired by three passages through the glass was 36°, while that acquired by five passages was 60°. But even when this method of magnifying was applied, he failed with various solid substances to obtain any effect; and in the case of air, though he employed to the utmost the power which these repeated reflections placed in his hands, he failed to produce the slightest sensible rotation.

These failures of Faraday to obtain the effect with gases seem to indicate the true seat of the phenomenon. The luminiferous ether surrounds and is influenced by the ultimate particles of matter. The symmetry of the one involves that of the other. Thus, if the molecules of a crystal be perfectly symmetrical round any line through the crystal, we may safely conclude that a ray will pass along this line as through ordinary glass. It will not be doubly refracted. From the symmetry of the liquid figures, known to be produced in the planes of freezing when radiant heat is sent through ice, we may safely infer symmetry of aggregation, and hence conclude that the line perpendicular to the planes of freezing is a line of no double refraction; that it is, in fact, the optic axis of the crystal. The same remark applies to the line joining the opposite blunt angles of a crystal of Iceland spar. The arrangement of the molecules round this line being symmetrical, the condition of the ether depending upon these molecules shares their symmetry; and there is, therefore, no reason why the wave length should alter with the alteration of the azimuth round this line. Annealed glass has its molecules symmetrically arranged round every line that can be drawn through it; hence it is not doubly refractive. But let the substance be either squeezed or strained in one direction, the molecular symmetry, and with it the symmetry of the ether, is immediately destroyed and the glass becomes doubly refractive. Unequal heating produces the same effect. Thus mechanical strains reveal themselves by optical effects; and there is

In the case of ordinary light shining at an angle upon a flat piece of heat-treated glass, there is no evidence to the eye that any strain may exist between the glass particles. Under polarized light, rays reflected from the upper glass surface can interfere with those from the lower glass surface, to produce optical effects. The one pictured is for a flat triangle of annealed glass that shows a symmetrical mechanical strain.

little doubt that in Faraday's experiment it is the *magnetic strain* that produces the rotation of the plane of polarization.*

---

* The power of double refraction conferred on the center of a glass rod, when it is caused to sound the fundamental note due to its longitudinal vibration, and the absence of the same power in the case of vibrating air (enclosed in a glass organ-pipe), seems to be analogous to the presence and absence of Faraday's effect in the same two substances.

Faraday never, to my knowledge, attempted to give, even in conversation, a picture of the molecular condition of his heavy glass when subjected to magnetic influence. In a mathematical investigation of the subject, published in the *Proceedings of the Royal Society* for 1856, Sir William Thomson arrives at the conclusion that the "diamagnetic" is in a state of molecular *rotation*.

Discovery of Diamagnetism; Researches on Magnecrystallic Action

Faraday's next great step in discovery was announced in a memoir on the "magnetic condition of all matter," communicated to the Royal Society on December 18, 1845. One great source of his success was the employment of extraordinary power. As already stated, he never accepted a negative answer to an experiment until he had brought to bear upon it all the force at his command. He had over and over again tried steel magnets and ordinary electromagnets on various substances, but without detecting anything different from the ordinary attraction exhibited by a few of them. Stronger coercion, however, developed a new action. Before the pole of an electromagnet, he suspended a fragment of his famous heavy glass; and observed that when the magnet was powerfully excited the glass fairly retreated from the pole. It was a clear case of magnetic *repulsion*. He then suspended a bar of the glass between two poles; the bar retreated when the poles were excited, and set its length *equatorially* or at right angles to the line joining them. When an ordinary magnetic body was similarly suspended, it always set *axially*, that is, from pole to pole.

Faraday called those bodies which were repelled

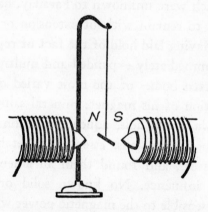

A bar of a diamagnetic substance, such as metallic bismuth, when placed in a strong magnetic field will set its length at right angles to the line joining the poles. It is a case of the magnet producing a repulsion.

by the poles of a magnet, *diamagnetic* bodies; using this term in a sense different from that in which he employed it in his memoir on the magnetization of light. The term *magnetic* he reserved for bodies which exhibited the ordinary attraction. He afterwards employed the term magnetic to cover the whole phenomena of attraction and repulsion, and used the word *paramagnetic* to designate such magnetic action as is exhibited by iron.

Isolated observations by Brugmans, Becquerel, Le Baillif, Saigy, and Seebeck had indicated the existence of a repulsive force exercised by the magnet on two or three substances; but these observations, which were unknown to Faraday, had been permitted to remain without extension or examination. Having laid hold of the fact of repulsion, Faraday immediately expanded and multiplied it. He subjected bodies of the most varied qualities to the action of his magnet: mineral salts, acids, alkalis, ethers, alcohols, aqueous solutions, glass, phosphorus, resins, oils, essences, vegetable and animal tissues, and found them all amenable to magnetic influence. No known solid or liquid proved insensible to the magnetic power when developed in sufficient strength. All the tissues of the human body, the blood—though it contains iron—included, were proved to be diamagnetic. So that if you could suspend a man between the poles of a magnet, his extremities would retreat from the poles until his length became equatorial.

Soon after he had commenced his researches on diamagnetism, Faraday noticed a remarkable phenomenon which first crossed my own path in the following way: In the year 1849, while working in the cabinet of my friend, Professor Knoblauch, of Marburg, I suspended a small copper coin between the poles of an electromagnet. On exciting the magnet, the coin moved towards the poles and then suddenly stopped, as if it had struck against a cushion. On breaking the circuit, the coin was repelled, the revulsion being so violent as to cause it to spin several times round its axis of suspension. A *Silbergroschen* [11] similarly suspended exhibited the same deportment. For a moment I thought this a new discovery; but on looking over the literature of the subject, it appeared that Faraday had observed, multiplied, and explained the same effect during his researches on diamagnetism. His explanation was based upon his own great discovery of magnetoelectric currents. The effect is a most singular one. A weight of several pounds of copper may be set spinning between the electromagnetic poles; the excitement of the magnet instantly stops the rotation. Though nothing is ap-

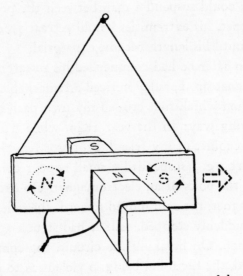

When a piece of heavy copper is swung as a pendulum to the right between the poles of a powerful electromagnet, its motion is almost suddenly stopped. Faraday explained the result as due to the effect of electric currents induced in the copper, shown in a dotted manner in the figure. The magnetic effect of the induced currents opposed the motion of the copper.

parent to the eye, the copper, if moved in the excited magnetic field, appears to move through a viscous fluid; while, when a flat piece of the metal is caused to pass to and fro like a saw between the poles, the sawing of the magnetic field resembles the cutting through of cheese or butter.* This

---

* See *Heat as a Mode of Motion*, ninth edition, page 75.

virtual *friction* of the magnetic field is so strong, that copper, by its rapid rotation between the poles, might probably be fused. We may easily dismiss this experiment by saying that the heat is due to the electric currents excited in the copper. But so long as we are unable to reply to the question, "What is an electric current?" the explanation is only provisional. For my own part, I look with profound interest and hope on the strange action here referred to.

Faraday's thoughts ran intuitively into experimental combinations, so that subjects whose capacity for experimental treatment would, to ordinary minds, seem to be exhausted in a moment, were shown by him to be all but inexhaustible. He has now an object in view, the first step towards which is the proof that the principle of Archimedes is true of magnetism. He forms magnetic solutions of various degrees of strength, places them between the poles of his magnet, and suspends in the solutions various magnetic bodies. He proves that when the solution is stronger than the body plunged in it, the body, though magnetic, is repelled; and when an elongated piece of it is surrounded by the solution, it sets, like a diamagnetic body, equatorially between the excited poles. The same body when suspended in a solution of weaker magnetic power than itself, is attracted as a whole, while an elongated portion of it sets axially.

And now theoretic questions rush in upon him. Is this new force a true repulsion, or is it merely a differential attraction? Might not the apparent repulsion of diamagnetic bodies be really due to the greater attraction of the medium by which they are surrounded? He tries the rarefaction of air, but finds the effect insensible. He is averse to ascribing a capacity of attraction to space, or to any hypothetical medium supposed to fill space. He therefore inclines, but still with caution, to the opinion that the action of a magnet upon bismuth is a true and absolute repulsion, and not merely the result of differential attraction. And then he clearly states a theoretic view sufficient to account for the phenomena. "Theoretically," he says, "an explanation of the movements of the diamagnetic bodies, and all the dynamic phenomena consequent upon the action of magnets upon them, might be offered in the supposition that magnetic induction caused in them a contrary state to that which it produced in ordinary matter." That is to say, while in ordinary magnetic influence the exciting pole excites adjacent to itself the contrary magnetism, in diamagnetic bodies the adjacent magnetism is the same as that of the exciting pole. This theory of reversed polarity, however, does not appear to have ever laid deep hold of Faraday's mind; and his own experiments failed to give any evidence of its truth. He therefore subsequently abandoned it, and maintained the *nonpolarity* of the diamagnetic force.

He then entered a new, though related, field of inquiry. Having dealt with the metals and their compounds, and having classified all of them that came within the range of his observation under the two heads magnetic and diamagnetic, he began the investigation of the phenomena presented by crystals when subjected to magnetic power. This action of crystals had been in part theoretically predicted by Poisson,* and actually discovered by Plücker, whose beautiful results, at the period which we have now reached, profoundly interested all scientific men. Faraday had been frequently puzzled by the deportment of bismuth, a highly crystalline metal. Sometimes elongated masses of the substance refused to set equatorially, sometimes they set persistently oblique, and sometimes even, like a magnetic body, from pole to pole. "The effect," he says, "occurs at a single pole; and it is then striking to observe a long piece of a substance so

---

* See Sir William Thomson on magnecrystallic action. *Philosophical Magazine*, 1851.

diamagnetic as bismuth repelled, and yet at the same moment set round with force, axially, or end on, as a piece of magnetic substance would do." The effect perplexed him; and in his efforts to release himself from this perplexity, no feature of this new manifestation of force escaped his attention. His experiments are described in a memoir communicated to the Royal Society on December 7, 1848.

I have worked long myself at magnecrystallic action, amid all the light of Faraday's and Plücker's researches. The papers now before me were objects of daily and nightly study with me eighteen or nineteen years ago; but even now, though their perusal is but the last of a series of repetitions, they astonish me. Every circumstance connected with the subject; every shade of deportment; every variation in the energy of the action; almost every application which could possibly be made of magnetism to bring out in detail the character of this new force, is minutely described. The field is swept clean, and hardly anything experimental is left for the gleaner. The phenomena, he concludes, are altogether different from those of magnetism or diamagnetism: they would appear, in fact, to present to us "a new force, or a new form of force, in the molecules of matter," which, for convenience sake, he designates by a new word, as "the *magnecrystallic* force."

He looks at the crystal acted upon by the magnet. From its mass he passes, in idea, to its atoms, and he asks himself whether the power which can thus seize upon the crystalline molecules, after they have been fixed in their proper positions by crystallizing force, may not, when they are free, be able to determine their arrangement? He, therefore, liberates the atoms by fusing the bismuth. He places the fused substance between the poles of an electromagnet, powerfully excited; but he fails to detect any action. I think it cannot be doubted that an action is exerted here, that a true cause comes into play; but its magnitude is not such as sensibly to interfere with the force of crystallization, which, in comparison with the diamagnetic force, is enormous. "Perhaps," adds Faraday, "if a longer time were allowed, and a permanent magnet used, a better result might be obtained. I had built many hopes upon the process." This expression, and his writings abound in such, illustrates what has been already said regarding his experiments being suggested and guided by his theoretic conceptions. His mind was full of hopes and hypotheses, but he always brought them to an experimental test. The record of his planned and executed experiments would, I doubt not, show a high ratio of hopes disappointed to hopes fulfilled; but every case of fulfilment abolished all memory of defeat; disappointment was swallowed up in victory.

After the description of the general character of this new force, Faraday states—with the emphasis here reproduced—its mode of action: "The *law* of action appears to be that *the line or axis* of MAGNECRYSTALLIC *force* (being the resultant of the action of all the molecules) *tends to place itself parallel, or as a tangent, to the magnetic curve, or line of magnetic force, passing through the place where the crystal is situated.*" The magnecrystallic force, moreover, appears to him "to be clearly distinguished from the magnetic or diamagnetic forces, in that it causes neither approach nor recession, consisting not in attraction or repulsion, but in giving a certain determinate position to the mass under its influence." And then he goes on "very carefully to examine and prove the conclusion that there was no connection of the force with attractive or repulsive influences." With the most refined ingenuity he shows that, under certain circumstances, the magnecrystallic force can cause the center of gravity of a highly magnetic body to retreat from the poles, and the center of gravity of a highly diamagnetic body to approach them. His experiments root his mind more and more firmly in the conclusion that "neither attraction nor repulsion causes the set, or governs the final position" of the crystal in the magnetic field. That the force which does so is therefore "distinct in its character and effects from the magnetic and diamagnetic forms of force. On the other hand," he continues, "it has a most manifest relation to the crystalline structure of bismuth and other bodies, and therefore to the power by which their molecules are able to build up the crystalline masses."

And here follows one of those expressions which characterize the conceptions of Faraday in regard to force generally: "It appears to me impossible to conceive of the results in any other way than by a mutual reaction of the magnetic force, and the force of the particles of the crystals upon each other." He proves that the action of the force, though thus molecular, is an action at a distance; he shows that a bismuth crystal can cause a freely suspended magnetic needle to set parallel to its magnecrystallic axis. Few living men are aware of the difficulty of obtaining results like this, or of the delicacy necessary to their attainment. "But though it thus takes up the character of a force

acting at a distance, still it is due to that power of
the particles which makes them cohere in regular
order and gives the mass its crystalline aggregation,
which we call at other times the attraction of
aggregation, and so often speak of as acting at
insensible distances." Thus he broods over this new
force, and looks at it from all possible points of
inspection. Experiment follows experiment, as
thought follows thought. He will not relinquish
the subject as long as a hope exists of throwing
more light upon it. He knows full well the anom-
alous nature of the conclusion to which his experiments lead him. But experiment to him is final,
and he will not shrink from the conclusion. "This
force," he says, "appears to me to be very strange
and striking in its character. It is not polar, for
there is no attraction or repulsion." And then, as
if startled by his own utterance, he asks—"What
is the nature of the mechanical force which turns
the crystal round, and makes it affect a magnet?"
. . . "I do not remember," he continues, "hereto-
fore such a case of force as the present one, where
a body is brought into position only, without attraction or repulsion."

Plücker, the celebrated geometer already mentioned, who pursued experimental physics for
many years of his life with singular devotion and

success, visited Faraday in those days, and repeated before him his beautiful experiments on magneto-optic action. Faraday repeated and verified Plücker's observations, and concluded, what he at first seemed to doubt, that Plücker's results and magne-crystallic action had the same origin.

At the end of his papers, when he takes a last look along the line of research, and then turns his eyes to the future, utterances quite as much emotional as scientific escape from Faraday. "I cannot," he says, at the end of his first paper on magnecrystallic action, "conclude this series of researches without remarking how rapidly the knowledge of molecular forces grows upon us, and how strikingly every investigation tends to develop more and more their importance, and their extreme attraction as an object of study. A few years ago magnetism was to us an occult power, affecting only a few bodies; now it is found to influence all bodies, and to possess the most intimate relations with electricity, heat, chemical action, light, crystallization, and through it, with the forces concerned in cohesion; and we may, in the present state of things, well feel urged to continue in our labors, encouraged by the hope of bringing it into a bond of union with gravity itself."

Supplementary Remarks

A BRIEF SPACE will, perhaps, be granted me here to state the further progress of an investigation which interested Faraday so much. Drawn by the fame of Bunsen as a teacher, in the year 1848 I became a student in the University of Marburg, in Hesse Cassel. Bunsen's behavior to me was that of a brother as well as that of a teacher, and it was also my happiness to make the acquaintance and gain the friendship of Professor Knoblauch, so highly distinguished by his researches on radiant heat. Plücker's and Faraday's investigations filled all minds at the time, and towards the end of 1849, Professor Knoblauch and myself commenced a joint investigation of the entire question. Long discipline was necessary to give us due mastery over it. Employing a method proposed by Dove, we examined the optical properties of our crystals ourselves; and these optical observations went hand in hand with our magnetic experiments. The number of these experiments was very great, but for a considerable time no fact of importance was added to those already published. At length, however, it was our fortune to meet with various crystals whose deportment could not be brought under the laws of magnecrystallic action enunciated by Plücker. We also discovered instances which led us to suppose that the magnecrystallic force was by no means independent, as alleged, of the magnetism or diamagnetism of the mass of the crystal. Indeed, the more we worked at the subject, the more clearly did it appear to us that the deportment of crystals in the magnetic field was due, not to a force previously unknown, but to the modification of the known forces of magnetism and diamagnetism by crystalline aggregation.

An eminent example of magnecrystallic action adduced by Plücker, and experimented on by Faraday, was Iceland spar. It is what in optics is called a *negative* crystal, and according to the law of Plücker, the axis of such a crystal was always repelled by a magnet. But we showed that it was only necessary to substitute, in whole or in part, carbonate of iron for carbonate of lime, thus changing the magnetic but not the optical character of the crystal, to cause the axis to be attracted. That the deportment of magnetic crystals is exactly antithetical to that of diamagnetic crystals isomorphous with the magnetic ones, was proved to be a general law of action. In all cases, the line which in a diamagnetic crystal set equatorially, always set itself in an isomorphous magnetic crystal axially. By mechanical compression other bodies were also made to imitate the Iceland spar.

These and numerous other results bearing upon the question were published at the time in the *Philosophical Magazine* and in *Poggendorff's Annalen;* and the investigation of diamagnetism and magnecrystallic action was subsequently continued by me in the laboratory of Professor Magnus of Berlin. In December, 1851, after I had quitted Germany, Dr. Bence Jones went to the Prussian capital to see the celebrated experiments of Du Bois Reymond. Influenced, I suppose, by what he there heard, he afterwards invited me to give a Friday evening discourse at the Royal Institution. I consented, not without fear and trembling. For the Royal Institution was to me a kind of dragon's den, where tact and strength would be necessary to save me from destruction. On February 11, 1853, the discourse was given, and it ended happily. I allude to these things, that I may mention that, though my aim and object in that lecture was to subvert the notions both of Faraday and Plücker, and to establish in opposition to their views what I regarded as the truth, it was very far from producing in Faraday either enmity or anger. At the conclusion of the lecture, he quitted his accustomed seat, crossed the theater to the corner into which I had shrunk, shook me by the hand, and brought me back to the table. Once more, subsequently, and in connection with a related question, I ventured to differ from him still more emphatically. It was done out of trust in the greatness of his character; nor was the trust misplaced. He felt my public dissent from him; and it pained me afterwards to the quick to think that I had given him even momentary annoyance. It was, however, only momentary. His soul was above all littleness and proof to all egotism. He was the same to me afterwards that he had been before; the very chance expression which led me to conclude that he felt my dissent being one of kindness and affection.

It required long subsequent effort to subdue the

complications of magnecrystallic action, and to bring under the dominion of elementary principles the vast mass of facts which the experiments of Faraday and Plücker had brought to light. It was proved by Reich, Edmond Becquerel, and myself, that the condition of diamagnetic bodies, in virtue of which they were repelled by the poles of a magnet, was excited in them by those poles; that the strength of this condition rose and fell with, and was proportional to, the strength of the acting magnet. It was not then any property possessed permanently by the bismuth, and which merely required the development of magnetism to act upon it, that caused the repulsion; for then the repulsion would have been simply proportional to the strength of the influencing magnet, whereas experiment proved it to augment as the square of the strength. The capacity to be repelled was therefore not inherent in the bismuth, but *induced*. So far an identity of action was established between magnetic and diamagnetic bodies. After this the deportment of magnetic bodies, "normal" and "abnormal"; crystalline, amorphous, and compressed, was compared with that of crystalline, amorphous, and compressed diamagnetic bodies; and by a series of experiments, executed in the laboratory of this Institution, the most complete antithesis was established between magnetism and diamagnetism. This antithesis embraced the quality of polarity—the theory of reversed polarity, first propounded by Faraday, being proved to be true. The discussion of the question was very brisk. On the Continent Professor Wilhelm Weber was the ablest and most successful supporter of the doctrine of diamagnetic polarity; and it was with an apparatus, devised by him and constructed under his own superintendence, by Leyser of Leipzig, that the last demands of the opponents of diamagnetic polarity were satisfied. The establishment of this point was absolutely necessary to the explanation of magnecrystallic action.

With that admirable instinct which always guided him, Faraday had seen that it was possible, if not probable, that the diamagnetic force acts with different degrees of intensity in different directions, through the mass of a crystal. In his studies on electricity, he had sought an experimental reply to the question whether crystalline bodies had not different specific inductive capacities in different directions, but he failed to establish any difference of the kind. His first attempt to establish differences of diamagnetic action in different directions through bismuth, was also a failure; but he must have felt this to be a point of cardinal importance, for he returned to the subject in 1850, and proved that bismuth was repelled with different degrees of force in different directions. It seemed as if the crystal were compounded of two diamagnetic bodies of different strengths, the substance being more strongly repelled across the magnecrystallic axis than along it. The same result was obtained independently, and extended to various other bodies, magnetic as well as diamagnetic, and also to compressed substances, a little subsequently by myself.

The law of action in relation to this point is, that in diamagnetic crystals, the line along which the repulsion is a maximum, sets equatorially in the magnetic field; while in magnetic crystals the line along which the attraction is a maximum sets from pole to pole. Faraday had said that the magnecrystallic force was neither attraction nor repulsion. Thus far he was right. It was neither taken singly, *but it was both.* By the combination of the doctrine of diamagnetic polarity with these differential attractions and repulsions, and by paying due regard to the character of the magnetic field, every fact brought to light in the domain of magnecrystallic action received complete explanation. The most perplexing of those facts were shown to result from the action of mechanical couples, which the proved polarity both of magnetism and diamagnetism brought into play. Indeed the thoroughness with which the experiments of Faraday were thus explained, is the most striking possible demonstration of the marvellous precision with which they were executed.

Magnetism of Flame and Gases;
Atmospheric Magnetism

WHEN AN experimental result was obtained by Faraday it was instantly enlarged by his imagination. I am acquainted with no mind whose power and suddenness of expansion at the touch of new physical truth could be ranked with his. Sometimes I have compared the action of his experiments on his mind to that of highly combustible matter thrown into a furnace; every fresh entry of fact was accompanied by the immediate development of light and heat. The light, which was intellectual, enabled him to see far beyond the boundaries of the fact itself, and the heat, which was emotional, urged him to the conquest of this newly revealed domain. But though the force of his imagination was enormous, he bridled it like a mighty rider, and never permitted his intellect to be overthrown.

In virtue of the expansive power which his vivid imagination conferred upon him, he rose from the smallest beginnings to the grandest ends. Having heard from Zantedeschi that Bancalari had established the magnetism of flame, he repeated the experiments and augmented the results. He passed from flames to gases, examining and revealing their magnetic and diamagnetic powers; and then he suddenly rose from his bubbles of oxygen and nitrogen to the atmospheric envelope of the earth itself, and its relations to the great question of terrestrial magnetism. The rapidity with which these ever-augmenting thoughts assumed the form of experiments is unparalleled. His power in this respect is often best illustrated by his minor investigations, and, perhaps, by none more strikingly than by his paper "On the Diamagnetic Condition of Flame and Gases," published as a letter to Mr. Richard Taylor, in the *Philosophical Magazine* for December, 1847. After verifying, varying, and expanding the results of Bancalari, he submitted to examination heated air currents, produced by platinum spirals placed in the magnetic field, and raised to incandescence by electricity. He then examined the magnetic deportment of gases generally. Almost all of these gases are invisible; but he must, nevertheless, track them in their unseen courses. He could not effect this by mingling smoke with his gases, for the action of his magnet upon the smoke would have troubled his conclusions. He, therefore, "caught" his gases in tubes, carried them out of the magnetic field, and made them reveal themselves at a distance from the magnet.

Immersing one gas in another, he determined their differential action; results of the utmost beauty being thus arrived at. Perhaps the most important are those obtained with atmospheric air and its two constituents. *Oxygen,* in various media, was strongly attracted by the magnet; in coal gas, for example, it was powerfully magnetic, whereas *nitrogen* was diamagnetic. Some of the effects obtained with oxygen in coal gas were strikingly beautiful. When the fumes of chloride of ammonium (a diamagnetic substance) were mingled with the oxygen, the cloud of chloride behaved in a most singular manner— "The attraction of iron filings," says Faraday, "to a magnetic pole is not more striking than the appearance presented by the oxygen under these circumstances."

On observing this deportment the question immediately occurs to him: Can we not separate the oxygen of the atmosphere from its nitrogen by magnetic analysis? It is the perpetual occurrence of such questions that marks the great experimenter. The attempt to analyze atmospheric air by magnetic force proved a failure, like the previous attempt to influence crystallization by the magnet. The enormous comparative power of the force of crystallization I have already assigned as a reason for the incompetence of the magnet to determine molecular arrangement; in the present instance the magnetic analysis is opposed by the force of diffusion, which is also very strong comparatively. The same remark applies to, and is illustrated by, another experiment subsequently executed by Faraday. Water is diamagnetic, sulphate of iron is strongly magnetic. He enclosed "a dilute solution of sulphate of iron in a tube, and placed the lower end of the tube between the poles of a powerful horseshoe magnet for days together," but he could produce "no concentration of the solution in the part near the magnet." Here also the diffusibility of the salt was too powerful for the force brought against it.

The experiment last referred to is recorded in

a paper presented to the Royal Society on the 2nd August, 1850, in which he pursues the investigation of the magnetism of gases. Newton's observations on soap bubbles were often referred to by Faraday. His delight in a soap bubble was like that of a boy, and he often introduced them into his lectures, causing them, when filled with air, to float on invisible seas of carbonic acid, and otherwise employing them as a means of illustration. He now finds them exceedingly useful in his experiments on the magnetic condition of gases. A bubble of air in a magnetic field occupied by air was unaffected, save through the feeble repulsion of its envelope. A bubble of nitrogen, on the contrary, was repelled from the magnetic axis with a force far surpassing that of a bubble of air. The deportment of oxygen in air "was very impressive, the bubble being pulled inward or towards the axial line, sharply and suddenly, as if the oxygen were highly magnetic."

He next labors to establish the true magnetic zero, a problem not so easy as might at first sight be imagined. For the action of the magnet upon any gas, while surrounded by air or any other gas, can only be differential; and if the experiment were made *in vacuo*, the action of the envelope, in this case necessarily of a certain thickness, would trouble the result. While dealing with this subject, Faraday makes some noteworthy observations regarding *space*. In reference to the Torricellian vacuum, he says, "Perhaps it is hardly necessary for me to state that I find both iron and bismuth in such vacua perfectly obedient to the magnet. From such experiments, and also from general observations and knowledge, it seems manifest that the lines of magnetic force can traverse pure space, just as gravitating force does, and as statical electrical forces do, and therefore space has a magnetic relation of its own, and one that we shall probably find hereafter to be of the utmost importance in natural phenomena. But this character of space is not of the same kind as that which, in relation to matter, we endeavor to express by the terms magnetic and diamagnetic. To confuse these together would be to confound space with matter, and to trouble all the conceptions by which we endeavor to understand and work out a progressively clearer view of the mode of action, and the laws of natural forces. It would be as if in gravitation or electric forces, one were to confound the particles acting on each other with the space across which they are acting, and would, I think, shut the door to advancement. Mere space cannot act as matter acts, even though the utmost latitude be allowed to the hypothesis of an ether; and admitting that hypothesis, it would be a large additional assumption to suppose that the lines of magnetic force are vibrations carried on by it, whilst as yet we have no proof that time is required for their propagation, or in what respect they may, in general character, assimilate to or differ from the respective lines of gravitating, luminiferous, or electric forces."

Pure space he assumes to be the true magnetic zero, but he pushes his inquiries to ascertain whether among material substances there may not be some which resemble space. If you follow his experiments, you will soon emerge into the light of his results. A torsion beam was suspended by a skein of cocoon silk; at one end of the beam was fixed a crosspiece 1½ inch long. Tubes of exceedingly thin glass, filled with various gases, and hermetically sealed, were suspended in pairs from the two ends of the crosspiece. The position of the rotating torsion head was such that the two tubes were at opposite sides of, and equidistant from, the magnetic axis, that is to say from the line joining the two closely approximated polar points of an electromagnet. His object was to compare the magnetic action of the gases in the two tubes. When one tube was filled with oxygen, and the other with nitrogen, on the supervention of the

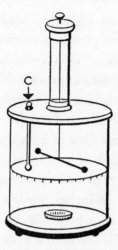

*In many of his experiments Faraday used a torsion balance.
The figure shows this balance in use as an electroscope for the
accurate measuring of small electrical charges. The main
feature is the use of a fine filament of metal, glass, or cocoon
silk that is twisted by the rotation of the torsion beam at the
bottom of the filament. The filament resists this twist and
returns to its first position when the action is over. The
extent of the twist is measured in degrees, marked on the
glass of the instrument. The charge to be measured is placed
on knob C and spreads to the metal-covered ball below.
A ball on the torsion beam is turned in position to touch the
other. It is then repelled, electrically, twisting the filament.
The torsion head at the top is used to turn the torsion beam
in making the needed contact.*

magnetic force, the oxygen was pulled towards the
axis, the nitrogen being pushed out. By turning
the torsion head they could be restored to their

primitive position of equidistance, where it is evident the action of the glass envelopes was annulled. The amount of torsion necessary to re-establish equidistance expressed the *magnetic difference* of the substances compared.

And then he compared oxygen with oxygen at different pressures. One of his tubes contained the gas at the pressure of 30 inches of mercury, another at a pressure of 15 inches of mercury, a third at a pressure of 10 inches, while a fourth was exhausted as far as a good air pump renders exhaustion possible. "When the first of these was compared with the other three, the effect was most striking." It was drawn towards the axis when the magnet was excited, the tube containing the rarer gas being apparently driven away, and the greater the difference between the densities of the two gases, the greater was the energy of this action.

And now observe his mode of reaching a *material* magnetic zero. When a bubble of nitrogen was exposed in air in the magnetic field, on the supervention of the power, the bubble retreated from the magnet. A less acute observer would have set nitrogen down as diamagnetic; but Faraday knew that retreat, in a medium composed in part of oxygen, might be due to the attraction of the latter gas, instead of to the repulsion of the gas immersed in it. But if nitrogen be really diamagnetic, then a bubble or bulb filled with the dense gas will overcome one filled with the rarer gas. From the crosspiece of his torsion balance he suspended his bulbs of nitrogen, at equal distances from the magnetic axis, and found that the rarefaction, or the condensation of the gas in either of the bulbs had not the slightest influence. When the magnetic force was developed, the bulbs remained in their first position, even when one was *filled* with nitrogen, and the other as far as possible *exhausted*. Nitrogen, in fact, acted "like space itself"; it was neither magnetic nor diamagnetic.

He cannot conveniently compare the paramagnetic force of oxygen with iron, in consequence of the exceeding magnetic intensity of the latter substance; but he does compare it with the sulphate of iron, and finds that, bulk for bulk, oxygen is equally magnetic with a solution of this substance in water "containing seventeen times the weight of the oxygen in crystallized protosulphate of iron, or 3.4 times its weight of metallic iron in that state of combination." By its capability to deflect a fine glass fiber, he finds that the attraction of this bulb of oxygen, containing only 0.117 of a grain of the gas, at an average distance of more than an inch from the magnetic axis, is about equal to the gravitating force of the same amount of oxygen as expressed by its weight.

These facts could not rest for an instant in the mind of Faraday without receiving that expansion to which I have already referred. "It is hardly necessary," he writes, "for me to say here that this oxygen cannot exist in the atmosphere exerting such a remarkable and high amount of magnetic force, without having a most important influence on the disposition of the magnetism of the earth, as a planet; especially if it be remembered that its magnetic condition is greatly altered by variations of its density and by variations of its temperature. I think I see here the real cause of many of the variations of that force, which have been, and are now so carefully watched on different parts of the surface of the globe. The daily variation, and the annual variation, both seem likely to come under it; also very many of the irregular continual variations, which the photographic process of record renders so beautifully manifest. If such expectations be confirmed, and the influence of the atmosphere be found able to produce results like these, then we shall probably find a new relation between the aurora borealis and the magnetism of the earth, namely, a relation established, more or less, through the air itself in connection with the space above it; and even magnetic relations and variations, which are not as yet suspected, may be suggested and rendered manifest and measurable, in the further development of what I will venture to call *atmospheric magnetism*. I may be over-sanguine in these expectations, but as yet I am sustained in them by the apparent reality, simplicity, and sufficiency of the cause assumed, as it at present appears to my mind. As soon as I have submitted these views to a close consideration, and the test of accordance with observation, and, where applicable, with experiments also, I will do myself the honor to bring them before the Royal Society."

Two elaborate memoirs are then devoted to the subject of atmospheric magnetism; the first sent to the Royal Society on the 9th of October, and the second on the 19th of November, 1850. In these memoirs he discusses the effects of heat and cold upon the magnetism of the air, and the action on the magnetic needle, which must result from thermal changes. By the convergence and divergence of the lines of terrestrial magnetic force, he shows how the distribution of magnetism, in the earth's atmosphere, is effected. He applies his results to the explanation of the annual and of the diurnal variation: he also considers irregular variations, including the action of magnetic storms. He discusses, at length, the observations at Saint Petersburg, Greenwich, Hobarton, Saint Helena, Toronto, and the Cape of Good Hope; believing that the facts, revealed by his experiments, furnish the key to the variations observed at all these places.

In the year 1851, I had the honor of an interview with Humboldt, in Berlin, and his parting words to me then were, "Tell Faraday that I entirely agree with him, and that he has, in my opinion, completely explained the variation of the declination." Eminent men have since informed me that Humboldt was hasty in expressing this opinion. In fact, Faraday's memoirs on atmospheric magnetism lost much of their force—perhaps too much—through the important discovery of the relation of the variation of the declination to the number of the solar spots. But I agree with him and M. Edmond Becquerel, who worked independently at this subject, in thinking, that a body so magnetic as oxygen, swathing the earth, and subject to variations of temperature, diurnal and annual, must affect the manifestations of terrestrial magnetism.* The air that stands upon a single square foot of the earth's surface is, according to Faraday, equivalent in magnetic

---

* This persuasion has been greatly strengthened by the recent perusal of a paper by Mr. Baxendell.

force to 8160 pounds of crystallized protosulphate of iron. Such a substance cannot be absolutely neutral as regards the deportment of the magnetic needle. But Faraday's writings on this subject are so voluminous, and the theoretic points are so novel and intricate, that I shall postpone the complete analysis of these researches to a time when I can lay hold of them more completely than my other duties allow me to do now.

Speculations; Nature of Matter; Lines of Force

THE SCIENTIFIC picture of Faraday would not be complete without a reference to his speculative writings. On Friday, January 19, 1844, he opened the weekly evening meetings of the Royal Institution by a discourse entitled, "A Speculation Touching Electric Conduction and the Nature of Matter." In this discourse he not only attempts the overthrow of Dalton's Theory of Atoms, but also the subversion of all ordinary scientific ideas regarding the nature and relations of matter and force. He objected to the use of the term atom: "I have not yet found a mind," he says, "that did habitually separate it from its accompanying temptations; and there can be no doubt that the words definite proportions, equivalent, primes, etc., which did and do fully express all the *facts* of what is usually called the atomic theory in chemistry, were dismissed because they were not expressive enough, and did not say all that was in the mind of him who used the word atom in their stead."

A moment will be granted me to indicate my own view of Faraday's position here. The word "atom" was not used in the stead of definite proportions, equivalents, or primes. These terms represented facts that followed from, but were not equivalent to, the atomic theory. Facts cannot satisfy the mind; and, the law of definite combining proportions being once established, the question "Why should combination take place according to that law?" is inevitable. Dalton answered this question by the enunciation of the atomic theory, the fundamental idea of which is, in my opinion, perfectly secure. The objection of Faraday to Dalton might be urged with the same substantial force against Newton: it might be stated with regard to the planetary motions that the laws of Kepler revealed the *facts*; that the introduction of the principle of gravitation was an addition to the facts. But this is the essence of *all* theory. The theory is the backward guess from fact to principle, the conjecture or divination regarding something, which lies behind the facts, and from which they flow in necessary sequence. If Dalton's theory, then, accounts for the definite proportions observed in the combinations of chemistry, its justification rests upon the same basis as that of the principle of gravitation. All that can in strictness be said in either case is that the facts occur *as if* the principle existed.

The manner in which Faraday himself habitually deals with his hypotheses is revealed in this lecture. He incessantly employed them to gain experimental ends, but he incessantly took them down, as an architect removes the scaffolding when the edifice is complete. "I cannot but doubt," he says, "that he who as a mere philosopher has most power of penetrating the secrets of nature, *and guessing by hypothesis* at her mode of working, will also be most careful for his own safe progress and that of others, to distinguish the knowledge which consists of assumption, by which I mean theory and hypothesis, from that which is the knowledge of facts and laws." Faraday himself, in fact, was always "guessing by hypothesis," and making theoretic divination the stepping stone to his experimental results.

I have already more than once dwelt on the vividness with which he realized molecular conditions; we have a fine example of this strength and brightness of imagination in the present "speculation." He grapples with the notion that matter is made up of particles, not in absolute contact, but surrounded by interatomic space. "Space," he observes, "must be taken as the only *continuous part* of a body so constituted. Space will permeate all masses of matter in every direction like a net, except that in place of meshes it will form cells, isolating each atom from its neighbors, itself only being continuous."

Let us follow out this notion; consider, he argues, the case of a nonconductor of electricity, such for example as shellac, with its molecules and intermolecular spaces running through the mass. In its case space must be an insulator; for if it were a conductor it would resemble "*a fine metallic web*," penetrating the lac in every direction. But the fact is that it resembles the wax of black sealing wax, which surrounds and insulates the particles of conducting carbon, interspersed throughout its mass. In the case of shellac, therefore, *space is an insulator*.

But now, take the case of a conducting metal. Here we have, as before, the swathing of space round every atom. If space be an insulator there can be no transmission of electricity from atom to atom. But there *is* transmission; hence *space is a conductor*. Thus he endeavors to hamper the atomic theory. "The reasoning," he says, "ends in a subversion of that theory altogether; for if space be an insulator it cannot exist in conducting bodies, and if it be a conductor it cannot exist in insulating bodies. Any ground of reasoning," he adds, as if carried away by the ardor of argument, "which tends to such conclusions as these must in itself be false."

He then tosses the atomic theory from horn to horn of his dilemmas. What do we know, he asks, of the atom apart from its force? You imagine a nucleus which may be called *a*, and surround it by forces which may be called *m*. "To my mind the *a* or nucleus vanishes, and the substance consists in the powers of *m*. And indeed what notion can we form of the nucleus independent of its powers? What thought remains on which to hang the imagination of an *a* independent of the acknowledged forces?" Like Boscovich, he abolishes the atom, and puts a "center of force" in its place.

With his usual courage and sincerity he pushes his view to its utmost consequences. "This view of the constitution of matter," he continues, "would seem to involve necessarily the conclusion that matter fills all space, or at least all space to which gravitation extends; for gravitation is a property of matter dependent on a certain force, and it is this force which constitutes the matter. In that view matter is not merely mutually penetrable; * but each atom extends, so to say, throughout the whole of the solar system, yet always retaining its own center of force."

It is the operation of a mind filled with thoughts of this profound, strange, and subtle character that we have to take into account in dealing with Faraday's later researches. A similar cast of thought pervades a letter addressed by Faraday to Mr. Richard Phillips, and published in the *Philosophical Magazine* for May, 1846. It is entitled "Thoughts on Ray Vibrations," and it contains one of the most singular speculations that ever emanated from a scientific mind. It must be remembered here, that though Faraday lived amid such speculations he did not rate them highly, and that he was prepared at any moment to change them or let them go. They spurred him on, but

---

* He compares the interpenetration of two atoms to the coalescence of two distinct waves, which though for a moment blended to a single mass, preserve their individuality, and afterwards separate.

they did not hamper him. His theoretic notions were *fluent*; and when minds less plastic than his own attempted to render those fluxional images rigid, he rebelled. He warns Phillips moreover, that from first to last, "he merely threw out as matter for speculation the vague impressions of his mind; for he gave nothing as the result of sufficient consideration, or as the settled conviction, or even probable conclusion at which he had arrived."

The gist of this communication is that gravitating force acts in lines across space, and that the vibrations of light and radiant heat consist in the tremors of these lines of force. "This notion," he says, "as far as it is admitted, will dispense with the ether, which in another view is supposed to be the medium in which these vibrations take place." And he adds further on, that his view "endeavors to dismiss the ether but not the vibrations." The idea here set forth is the natural supplement of his previous notion, that it is gravitating force which constitutes matter, each atom extending, so to say, throughout the whole of the solar system.

The letter to Mr. Phillips winds up with this beautiful conclusion:

"I think it likely that I have made many mistakes in the preceding pages, for even to myself my ideas on this point appear only as the shadow of a speculation, or as one of those impressions upon the mind which are allowable for a time as guides to thought and research. He who labors in experimental inquiries knows how numerous these are, and how often their apparent fitness and beauty vanish before the progress and development of real natural truth."

Let it then be remembered that Faraday entertained notions regarding matter and force altogether distinct from the views generally held by scientific men. Force seemed to him an entity dwelling along the line in which it is exerted. The lines along which gravity acts between the sun and earth seem figured in his mind as so many elastic strings; indeed he accepts the assumed instantaneity of gravity as the expression of the enormous elasticity of the "lines of weight." Such views, fruitful in the case of magnetism, barren, as yet, in the case of gravity, explain his efforts to transform this latter force. When he goes into the open air and permits his helices to fall, to his mind's eye they are tearing through the lines of gravitating power, and hence his hope and conviction that an effect would and ought to be produced. It must ever be borne in mind that Faraday's difficulty in dealing with these conceptions was at bottom the same as that of Newton; that he is in fact trying to overleap this difficulty, and with it probably the limits prescribed to the intellect itself.

The idea of lines of magnetic force was suggested to Faraday by the linear arrangement of iron filings when scattered over a magnet. He speaks of—and illustrates by sketches—the deflection, both convergent and divergent, of the lines of force when they pass respectively through magnetic and diamagnetic bodies. These notions of concentration and divergence are also based on the direct observation of his filings. So long did he brood upon these lines; so habitually did he associate them with his experiments on induced currents, that the association became "indissoluble," and he could not think without them. "I have been so accustomed," he writes, "to employ them, and especially in my last researches, that I may have unwittingly become prejudiced in their favor, and ceased to be a clear-sighted judge. Still, I have always endeavored to make experiment the test and controller of theory and opinion; but neither by that nor by close cross-examination in principle, have I been made aware of any error involved in their use."

In his later researches on magnecrystallic action, the idea of lines of force is extensively employed; it indeed led him to an experiment which

lies at the root of the whole question. In his subsequent researches on atmospheric magnetism the
idea receives still wider application, showing itself
to be wonderfully flexible and convenient. Indeed without this conception the attempt to seize
upon the magnetic actions, possible or actual, of
the atmosphere would be difficult in the extreme;
but the notion of lines of force, and of their divergence and convergence, guides Faraday without perplexity through all the intricacies of the
question. After the completion of those researches,
and in a paper forwarded to the Royal Society on
October 22, 1851, he devotes himself to the formal
development and illustration of his favorite idea.
The paper bears the title, "On Lines of Magnetic
Force, Their Definite Character, and Their Distribution Within a Magnet and Through Space."
A deep reflectiveness is the characteristic of this
memoir. In his experiments, which are perfectly
beautiful and profoundly suggestive, he takes but
a secondary delight. His object is to illustrate the
utility of his conception of lines of force. "The
study of these lines," he says, "has at different times
been greatly influential in leading me to various
results which I think prove their utility as well as
fertility."

Faraday for a long period used the lines of force

merely as "a representative idea." He seemed for a time averse to going further in expression than the lines themselves, however much further he may have gone in idea. That he believed them to exist at all times round a magnet, and irrespective of the existence of magnetic matter, such as iron filings, external to the magnet, is certain. No doubt the space round every magnet presented itself to his imagination as traversed by loops of magnetic power; but he was chary in speaking of the physical substratum of those loops. Indeed it may be doubted whether the *physical theory* of lines of force presented itself with any distinctness to his own mind. The possible complicity of the luminiferous ether in magnetic phenomena was certainly in his thoughts. "How the magnetic force," he writes, "is transferred through bodies or through space we know not; whether the result is merely action at a distance, as in the case of gravity; or by some intermediate agency, as in the case of light, heat, the electric current, and (as I believe) static electric action. The idea of magnetic fluids, as applied by some, or of magnetic centers of action, does not include that of the latter kind of transmission, *but the idea of lines of force does.*" And he continues thus: "I am more inclined to the notion that in the transmission of the [magnetic] force there is such an action [an intermediate agency] external to the magnet, than that the effects are merely attraction and repulsion at a distance. *Such an affection may be a function of the ether; for it is not at all unlikely that, if there be an ether, it should have other uses than simply the conveyance of radiations.*" When he speaks of the magnet in certain cases, "revolving amongst its own forces," he appears to have some conception of this kind in view.

A great part of the investigation completed in October, 1851, was taken up with the motions of wires round the poles of a magnet and the converse. He carried an insulated wire along the axis of a bar magnet from its pole to its equator, where it issued from the magnet, and was bent up so as to connect its two ends. A complete circuit, no part of which was in contact with the magnet, was thus obtained. He found that when the magnet and the external wire were rotated together no current was produced; whereas, when *either* of them was rotated and the other left at rest currents were evolved. He then abandoned the axial wire, and allowed the magnet itself to take its place; the result was the same.* It was the *relative* motion

---

* In this form the experiment is identical with one made twenty years earlier. See page 35.

of the magnet and the loop that was effectual in producing a current.

The lines of force have their roots in the magnet, and though they may expand into infinite space, they eventually return to the magnet. Now these lines may be intersected close to the magnet or at a distance from it. Faraday finds *distance* to be perfectly immaterial so long as the *number* of lines intersected is the same. For example, when the loop connecting the equator and the pole of his bar magnet performs one complete revolution round the magnet, it is manifest that all the lines of force issuing from the magnet are *once* intersected. Now it matters not whether the loop be ten feet or ten inches in length, it matters not how it may be twisted and contorted, it matters not how near to the magnet or how distant from it the loop may be, one revolution always produces the same amount of current electricity, because in all these cases all the lines of force issuing from the magnet are *once* intersected and no more.

From the external portion of the circuit he passes in idea to the internal, and follows the lines of force into the body of the magnet itself. His conclusion is that there exist lines of force within the magnet of the same *nature* as those without. What is more, they are exactly equal in *amount* to those without. They have a relation in *direction* to those without; and in fact are continuations of them. . . . "Every line of force, therefore, at whatever distance it may be taken from the magnet, must be considered as a closed circuit, passing in some part of its course through the magnet, and having an equal amount of force in every part of its course."

All the results here described were obtained with *moving metals*. "But," he continues with profound sagacity, "mere motion would not generate a relation, which had not a foundation in the existence of some previous state; and therefore the *quiescent* metals must be in some relation to the active center of force," that is, to the magnet. He here touches the core of the whole question, and when we can state the condition into which the conducting wire is thrown *before* it is moved, we shall then be in a position to understand the physical constitution of the electric current generated by its motion.

In this inquiry Faraday worked with steel magnets, the force of which varies with the distance from the magnet. He then sought a *uniform field* of magnetic force, and found it in space as affected by the magnetism of the earth. His next memoir, sent to the Royal Society December 31, 1851, is

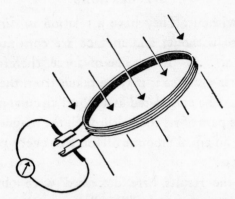

Faraday developed currents in rings or coils by merely rotating them across the lines of the magnetic force of the earth. Since the current would reverse in direction at every half revolution, he devised a special arrangement that kept the direction through the galvanometer constant.

"On the Employment of the Induced Magneto-electro Current as a Test and Measure of Magnetic Forces." He forms rectangles and rings, and by ingenious and simple devices collects the opposed currents which are developed in them by rotation across the terrestrial lines of magnetic force. He varies the shapes of his rectangles while preserving their areas constant, and finds that the constant area produces always the same amount of current per revolution. The current depends solely on the number of lines of force intersected, and when this number is kept constant the current remains constant too. Thus the lines of magnetic force are continually before his eyes, by their aid he colligates his facts, and through the inspirations derived from them he vastly expands the boundaries of our experimental knowledge. The beauty and exactitude of the results of this investigation are extraordinary. I cannot help thinking while I dwell upon them, that this discovery of magneto-electricity is the greatest experimental result ever obtained by an investigator. It is the Mont Blanc of Faraday's own achievements. He always worked at great elevations, but a higher than this he never subsequently attained.

Unity and Convertibility of Natural Forces; Theory of the Electric Current

THE TERMS *unity* and *convertibility*, as applied to natural forces, are often employed in these investigations, many profound and beautiful thoughts respecting these subjects being expressed in Faraday's memoirs. Modern inquiry has, however, much augmented our knowledge of the relationship of natural forces, and it seems worth while to say a few words here, tending to clear up certain misconceptions which appear to exist among philosophic writers regarding this relationship.

The whole stock of *energy* or *working power* in

the world consists of *attractions, repulsions,* and *motions.* If the attractions and repulsions are so circumstanced as to be able to produce motion, they are sources of working power, but not otherwise. Let us for the sake of simplicity confine our attention to the case of attraction. The attraction exerted between the earth and a body at a distance from the earth's surface is a source of working power; because the body can be moved by the attraction, and in falling to the earth can perform work. When it rests upon the earth's surface it is *not* a source of power or energy, because it can fall no further. But though it has ceased to be a source of *energy,* the attraction of gravity still acts as a *force,* which holds the earth and weight together.

The same remarks apply to attracting atoms and molecules. As long as distance separates them, they can move across it in obedience to the attraction, and the motion thus produced may, by proper appliances, be caused to perform mechanical work. When, for example, two atoms of hydrogen unite with one of oxygen to form water, the atoms are first drawn towards each other—they move, they clash, and then, by virtue of their resiliency, they recoil and *quiver.* To this quivering motion we give the name of heat. Now this quivering motion is merely the redistribution of the motion produced by the chemical affinity; and this is the only sense in which chemical affinity can be said to be converted into heat. We must not imagine the chemical *attraction* destroyed, or converted into anything else. For the atoms, when mutually clasped to form a molecule of water, are held together by the very attraction which first drew them towards each other. That which has really been expended is the *pull* exerted through the space by which the distance between the atoms has been diminished.

If this be understood, it will be at once seen that *gravity* may in this sense be said to be convertible into heat; that it is in reality no more an outstanding and inconvertible agent, as it is sometimes stated to be, than chemical affinity. By the exertion of a certain pull, through a certain space, a body is caused to clash with a certain definite velocity against the earth. Heat is thereby developed, and this is the only sense in which gravity can be said to be converted into heat. In no case is the *force* which produces the motion annihilated or changed into anything else. The mutual *attraction* of the earth and weight exists when they are in contact as when they were separate; but the ability of that attraction to employ itself in the production of motion does *not* exist.

The transformation, in this case, is easily followed by the mind's eye. First, the weight as a whole is set in motion by the attraction of gravity. This motion of the mass is arrested by collision with the earth, being broken up into molecular tremors, to which we give the name of heat.

And when we reverse the process, and employ those tremors of heat to raise a weight, as is done through the intermediation of an elastic fluid in the steam engine, a certain definite portion of the molecular motion is destroyed in raising the weight. In this sense, and this sense only, can the heat be said to be converted into gravity, or more correctly, into potential energy of gravity. It is not that the destruction of the heat has created any *new* attraction, but simply that the old attraction has now a power conferred upon it of exerting a certain definite pull in the interval between the starting point of the falling weight and its collision with the earth.

So also as regards magnetic attraction: when a sphere of iron placed at some distance from a magnet rushes towards the magnet and has its motion stopped by collision, an effect mechanically the same as that produced by the attraction of gravity occurs. The magnetic attraction generates the motion of the mass, and the stoppage of that motion produces heat. In this sense, and in this sense only, is there a transformation of magnetic work into heat. And if by the mechanical action of heat, brought to bear by means of a suitable machine, the sphere be torn from the magnet and again placed at a distance, a power of exerting a pull through that distance, and producing a new motion of the sphere, is thereby conferred upon the magnet; in this sense, and in this sense only, is the heat converted into magnetic potential energy.

When, therefore, writers on the conservation of energy speak of tensions being "consumed" and "generated," they do not mean thereby that old attractions have been annihilated and new ones brought into existence, but that, in the one case, the power of the attraction to produce motion has been diminished by the shortening of the distance between the attracting bodies, and that in the other case the power of producing motion has been augmented by the increase of the distance. These remarks apply to all bodies, whether they be sensible masses or molecules.

Of the inner quality that enables matter to attract matter we know nothing; and the law of conservation makes no statement regarding that quality. It takes the facts of attraction as they stand, and affirms only the constancy of *working power*. That power may exist in the form of MOTION; or it may exist in the form of FORCE, *with distance to act through*. The former is dynamic energy, the latter is potential energy, the constancy of the sum of both being affirmed by the law of conservation. The *convertibility* of natural forces consists solely in transformations of dynamic into potential, and of potential into dynamic, energy, which are incessantly going on. In no other sense has the convertibility of force, at present, any scientific meaning.

By the contraction of a muscle a man lifts a weight from the earth. But the muscle can contract only through the oxidation of its own tissue or of the blood passing through it. Molecular motion is thus converted into mechanical motion. Supposing the muscle to contract without raising the weight, oxidation would also occur, but the whole of the heat produced by this oxidation would be liberated *in the muscle itself*. Not so when it performs external work; to do that work a certain definite portion of the heat of oxidation must be expended. It is so expended in pulling the weight away from the earth. If the weight be permitted to fall, the heat generated by its collision with the earth would exactly make up for that lacking in the muscle during the lifting of the weight. In the case here supposed, we have a conversion of molecular muscular action into potential energy of gravity, and a conversion of that potential energy into heat—the heat, however, appearing at a distance from its real origin in the muscle. The whole process consists of a transference of molecular motion from the muscle to the weight, and gravitating force is the mere go-between, by means of which the transference is effected.

These considerations will help to clear our way to the conception of the transformations which occur when a wire is moved across the lines of force in a magnetic field. In this case it is commonly said we have a conversion of magnetism into electricity. But let us endeavor to understand what really occurs. For the sake of simplicity, and with a view to its translation into a different one subsequently, let us adopt for a moment the provisional conception of a mixed fluid in the wire, composed of positive and negative electricities in equal quantities, and therefore perfectly neutralizing each other when the wire is still. By the motion of the wire, say with the hand, towards the magnet, what the Germans call a *Scheidungskraft* —a separating force—is brought into play. This force tears the mixed fluids asunder, and drives them in two currents, the one positive and the other negative, in two opposite directions through the wire. The presence of these currents evokes a force of *repulsion* between the magnet and the wire; and to cause the one to approach the other, this repulsion must be overcome. The overcoming of this repulsion is, in fact, the work done in separating and impelling the two electricities. When the wire is moved away from the magnet, a *Scheidungskraft,* or separating force, also comes into play; but now it is an *attraction* that has to be surmounted. In surmounting it, currents are developed in directions opposed to the former; positive takes the place of negative, and negative the place of positive, the overcoming of the attraction being the work done in separating and impelling the two electricities.

The mechanical action occurring here is different from that occurring where a sphere of soft iron is withdrawn from a magnet, and again attracted. In this case muscular force is expended during the act of separation; but the attraction of the magnet effects the reunion. In the case of the moving wire also we overcome a resistance in separating it from the magnet, and thus far the action is mechanically the same as the separation of the sphere of iron. But after the wire has ceased moving, the attraction ceases; and so far from any action occurring similar to that which draws the iron sphere back to the magnet, we have to overcome a repulsion to bring them together.

There is no potential energy conferred either by the removal or by the approach of the wire, and the only power really transformed or converted, in the experiment, is muscular power. Nothing that could in strictness be called a conversion of magnetism into electricity occurs. The muscular oxidation that moves the wire fails to produce *within the muscle* its due amount of heat, a portion of that heat, equivalent to the resistance overcome, appearing in the moving wire instead.

Is this effect an attraction and a repulsion at a distance? If so, why should both cease when the wire ceases to move? In fact, the deportment of the wire resembles far more that of a body moving *in a resisting medium* than anything else; the resistance ceasing when the motion is suspended. Let us imagine the case of a liquid so mobile that the hand may be passed through it to and fro, without encountering any sensible resistance. It resembles the motion of a conductor in the unexcited field of an electromagnet. Now, let us suppose a body placed in the liquid, or acting on it, which confers upon it the property of *viscosity;* the hand would no longer move freely. During its motion, but then only, resistance would be encountered and overcome. Here we have rudely represented the case of the excited magnetic field, and the result in both cases would be substantially the same. In both cases heat would, in the end, be generated outside of the muscle, its amount being exactly equivalent to the resistance overcome.

Let us push the analogy a little further; suppose in the case of the fluid rendered viscous, as assumed a moment ago, the viscosity not to be so great as to prevent the formation of *ripples* when the hand is passed through the liquid. Then the motion of the hand, before its final conversion into heat, would exist for a time as wave motion, which, on subsiding, would generate its due equivalent of heat. This intermediate stage, in the case of our moving wire, is represented by the period *during which the electric current is flowing through it;* but that current, like the ripples of our liquid, soon subsides, being, like them, converted into heat.

Do these words shadow forth anything like the reality? Such speculations cannot be injurious if they are enunciated without dogmatism. I do confess that ideas such as these here indicated exercise a strong fascination on my mind. Is, then, the magnetic field really viscous, and if so, what substance exists in it and the wire to produce the viscosity? Let us first look at the proved effects, and afterwards turn our thoughts back upon their cause. When the wire approaches the magnet, an action is evoked within it, which travels through it with a velocity comparable to that of light. One substance only in the universe has been hitherto proved competent to transmit power at this velocity: the luminiferous ether. Not only its rapidity of progression, but its ability to produce the motion of light and heat, indicates that the electric current is also motion.* Further, there is a striking resemblance between the action of good and bad conductors as regards electricity, and the action of diathermanous and adiathermanous bodies as regards radiant heat. The good conductor is diathermanous to the electric current; it allows free transmission without the development of heat. The bad conductor is adiathermanous to the

---

* Mr. Clerk Maxwell has recently published an exceedingly important investigation connected with this question. Even in the nonmathematical portions of the memoirs of Mr. Maxwell, the admirable spirit of his philosophy is sufficiently revealed. As regards the employment of scientific imagery, I hardly know his equal in power of conception and clearness of definition.

electric current, and hence the passage of the latter is accompanied by the development of heat. I am strongly inclined to hold the electric current, pure and simple, to be a motion of the ether alone; good conductors being so constituted that the motion may be propagated through their ether without sensible transfer to their atoms, while in the case of bad conductors this transfer is effected, the transferred motion appearing as heat.*

I do not know whether Faraday would have subscribed to what is here written; probably his habitual caution would have prevented him from committing himself to anything so definite. But some such idea filled his mind and colored his language through all the later years of his life. I dare not say that he has been always successful in the treatment of these theoretic notions. In his speculations he mixes together light and darkness in varying proportions, and carries us along with him through strong alternations of both. It is impossible to say how a certain amount of mathematical training [12] would have affected his work.

---

* One important difference, of course, exists between the effect of motion in the magnetic field, and motion in a resisting medium. In the former case the heat is generated *in the moving conductor,* in the latter it is in part generated *in the medium.*

We cannot say what its influence would have been upon that force of inspiration that urged him on; whether it would have daunted him, and prevented him from driving his adits into places where no theory pointed to a lode. If so, then we may rejoice that this strong delver at the mine of natural knowledge was left free to wield his mattock in his own way. It must be admitted that Faraday's purely speculative writings often lack that precision which the mathematical habit of thought confers. Still across them flash frequent gleams of prescient wisdom which will excite admiration throughout all time; while the facts, relations, principles, and laws which his experiments have established are sure to form the body of grand theories yet to come.

Summary

WHEN FROM an Alpine height the eye of the climber ranges over the mountains, he finds that for the most part they resolve themselves into distinct groups, each consisting of a dominant mass surrounded by peaks of lesser elevation. The power which lifted the mightier eminences in nearly all cases lifted others to an almost equal height. And so it is with the discoveries of Faraday. As a general rule, the dominant result does not stand alone, but forms the culminating point of a vast and varied mass of inquiry. In this way, round about his great discovery of magnetoelectric induction, other weighty labors group themselves.

His investigations on the extra current, on the polar and other condition of diamagnetic bodies, on lines of magnetic force, their definite character and distribution, on the employment of the induced magnetoelectric current as a measure and test of magnetic action, on the revulsive phenomena of the magnetic field, are all, notwithstanding the diversity of title, researches in the domain of magnetoelectric induction.

Faraday's second group of researches and discoveries embrace the chemical phenomena of the current. The dominant result here is the great law of definite electrochemical decomposition, around which are massed various researches on electrochemical conduction and on electrolysis both with the machine and with the pile. To this group also belongs his analysis of the contact theory, his inquiries as to the source of voltaic electricity, and his final development of the chemical theory of the pile.

His third great discovery is the magnetization of light, which I should liken to the Weisshorn among mountains—high, beautiful, and alone.

The dominant result of his fourth group of researches is the discovery of diamagnetism, announced in his memoir as the magnetic condition of all matter, round which are grouped his inquiries on the magnetism of flame and gases; on magnecrystallic action, and on atmospheric magnetism, and its relations to the annual and diurnal variation of the needle, the full significance of which is still to be shown.

These are Faraday's most massive discoveries, and upon them his fame must mainly rest. But even without them, sufficient would remain to secure for him a high and lasting scientific reputation. We should still have his researches on the liquefaction of gases; on frictional electricity; on the electricity of the gymnotus; on the source of power in the hydroelectric machine, the last two investigations being untouched in the foregoing memoir; on electromagnetic rotations; on regelation; all his more purely chemical researches, including his discovery of benzol. Besides these he published a multitude of minor papers, most of which, in some way or other, illustrate his genius. I have made no allusion to his power and sweetness as a lecturer. Taking him for all in all, I think it will be conceded that Michael Faraday was the greatest experimental philosopher the world has ever seen; and I will add the opinion that the progress of future research will tend not to dim or to diminish, but to enhance and glorify the labors of this mighty investigator.

Illustrations of Character
and Conclusion

THUS FAR I have confined myself to topics mainly interesting to the man of science, endeavoring, however, to treat them in a manner unrepellent to the general reader who might wish to obtain a notion of Faraday as a worker. On others will fall the duty of presenting to the world a picture of the man. But I know you will permit me to add to the foregoing analysis a few personal reminiscences and remarks, tending to connect Faraday with a wider world than that of science —namely, with the general human heart.

One word in reference to his married life, in

addition to what has been already said, may find a place here. As in the former case, Faraday shall be his own spokesman. The following paragraph, though written in the third person, is from his hand: "On June 12, 1821, he married, an event which more than any other contributed to his earthly happiness and healthful state of mind. The union has continued for twenty-eight years and has in no wise changed, except in the depth and strength of its character."

Faraday's immediate forefathers lived in a little place called Clapham Wood Hall, in Yorkshire. Here dwelt Robert Faraday and Elizabeth his wife, who had ten children, one of them, James Faraday, born in 1761, being father to the philosopher. A family tradition exists that the Faradays came originally from Ireland. Faraday himself has more than once expressed to me his belief that his blood was in part Celtic, but how much of it was so, or when the infusion took place, he was unable to say. He could imitate the Irish brogue, and his wonderful vivacity may have been in part due to his extraction. But there were other qualities which we should hardly think of deriving from Ireland. The most prominent of these was his sense of order, which ran like a luminous beam through all the transactions of his life. The most entangled and complicated matters fell into harmony in his hands. His mode of keeping accounts excited the admiration of the managing board of this Institution. And his science was similarly ordered. In his *Experimental Researches*, he numbered every paragraph, and welded their various parts together by incessant reference. His private notes of the *Experimental Researches*, which are happily preserved, are similarly numbered: their last paragraph bears the figure 16,041. His working qualities, moreover, showed the tenacity of the Teuton. His nature was impulsive, but there was a force behind the impulse which did not permit it to retreat. If in his warm moments he formed a resolution, in his cool ones he made that resolution good. Thus his fire was that of a solid combustible, not that of a gas, which blazes suddenly, and dies as suddenly away.

And here I must claim your tolerance for the limits by which I am confined. No materials for a life of Faraday are in my hands, and what I have now to say has arisen almost wholly out of our close personal relationship.

Letters of his, covering a period of sixteen years, are before me, each one of which contains some characteristic utterance—strong, yet delicate in counsel, joyful in encouragement, and warm in affection. References which would be pleasant to such of them as still live are made to Humboldt, Biot, Dumas, Chevreul, Magnus, and Arago. Accident brought these names prominently forward; but many others would be required to complete his list of Continental friends. He prized the love and sympathy of men—prized it almost more than the renown which his science brought him. Nearly a dozen years ago it fell to my lot to write a review of his *Experimental Researches* for the *Philosophical Magazine*. After he had read it, he took me by the hand, and said, "Tyndall, the sweetest reward of my work is the sympathy and good will which it has caused to flow in upon me from all quarters of the world." Among his letters I find little sparks of kindness, precious to no one but myself, but more precious to me than all. He would peep into the laboratory when he thought me weary, and take me upstairs with him to rest. And if I happened to be absent, he would leave a little note for me, couched in this or some other similar form: "Dear Tyndall—I was looking for you, because we were at tea—we have not yet done—will you come up?" I frequently shared his early dinner; almost always, in fact, while my lectures were going on. There was no trace of asceticism in his nature. He preferred the meat and wine of life to its locusts and wild honey. Never once during an intimacy of fifteen years did he mention religion to me, save when I drew him on to the subject. He then spoke to me without hesitation or reluctance; not with any apparent desire to "improve the occasion," but to give me such information as I sought. He believed the human heart to be swayed by a power to which science or logic opened no approach, and, right or wrong, this faith, held in perfect tolerance of the faiths of others, strengthened and beautified his life.

From the letters just referred to, I will select three for publication here. I choose the first, because it contains a passage revealing the feelings with which Faraday regarded his vocation, and also because it contains an allusion which will give pleasure to a friend.

Royal Institution.
Ventnor, Isle of Wight, June 28, 1854.
My dear Tyndall—You see by the top of this letter how much habit prevails over me; I have just read yours from thence, and yet I think myself there. However, I have left its science in very good keeping, and I am glad to learn that you are at experiment once more. But how is the health? Not well, I fear. I wish you would get yourself strong first and work afterwards. As for the fruits, I am sure they will be good, for though I sometimes despond as regards myself, I

do not as regards you. You are young, I am old. . . . *But then our subjects are so glorious, that to work at them rejoices and encourages the feeblest; delights and enchants the strongest.*

I have not yet seen anything from Magnus. Thoughts of him always delight me. We shall look at this black sulphur together. I heard from Schonbein the other day. He tells me that Liebig is full of ozone, i.e., of allotropic oxygen.

Good-bye for the present.
Ever, my dear Tyndall,
Yours truly,
M. FARADAY

The contemplation of Nature, and his own relation to her, produced in Faraday a kind of spiritual exaltation which makes itself manifest here. His religious feeling and his philosophy could not be kept apart; there was an habitual overflow of the one into the other.

Whether he or another was its exponent, he appeared to take equal delight in science. A good experiment would make him almost dance with delight. In November, 1850, he wrote to me thus— "I hope some day to take up the point respecting the magnetism of associated particles. In the meantime I rejoice at every addition to the facts and reasoning connected with the subject. When science is a republic, then it gains; and though

I am no republican in other matters, I am in that."
All his letters illustrate this catholicity of feeling.
Ten years ago, when going down to Brighton, he
carried with him a little paper I had just completed, and afterwards wrote to me. His letter
is a mere sample of the sympathy which he always
showed to me and my work.

Brighton, December 9, 1857.

My dear Tyndall—I cannot resist the pleasure of saying how very much I have enjoyed your paper. Every
part has given me delight. It goes on from point to
point beautifully. You will find many pencil marks,
for I made them as I read. I let them stand, for though
many of them receive their answer as the story proceeds, yet they show how the wording impresses a mind
fresh to the subject, and perhaps here and there you
may like to alter it slightly, if you wish the full idea,
i.e., not an inaccurate one, to be suggested at first; and
yet after all I believe it is not your exposition, but the
natural jumping to a conclusion that affects or has affected my pencil.

We return on Friday, when I will return you the
paper.

Ever truly yours,
M. FARADAY

The third letter will come in its proper place
towards the end.

While once conversing with Faraday on science, in its relations to commerce and litigation, he said to me, that at a certain period of his career, he was forced definitely to ask himself, and finally to decide whether he should make wealth or science the pursuit of his life. He could not serve both masters, and he was therefore compelled to choose between them. After the discovery of magnetoelectricity his fame was so noised abroad that the commercial world would hardly have considered any remuneration too high for the aid of abilities like his. Even before he became so famous, he had done a little "professional business." This was the phrase he applied to his purely commercial work. His friend, Richard Phillips, for example, had induced him to undertake a number of analyses, which produced, in the year 1830, an addition to his income of more than a thousand pounds; and in 1831 a still greater addition. He had only to will it to raise in 1832 his professional business income to 5000 pounds a year. Indeed double this sum would be a wholly insufficient estimate of what he might, with ease, have realized annually during the last thirty years of his life.

While restudying the *Experimental Researches* with reference to the present memoir, the conversation with Faraday here alluded to came to my recollection, and I sought to ascertain the period when the question, "wealth or science," had presented itself with such emphasis to his mind. I fixed upon the year 1831 or 1832, for it seemed beyond the range of human power to pursue science as he had done during the subsequent years, and to pursue commercial work at the same time. To test this conclusion I asked permission to see his accounts, and on my own responsibility, I will state the result. In 1832, his professional business income, instead of rising to 5000 pounds, or more, fell from 1090 pounds 4 shillings to 155 pounds 9 shillings. From this it fell with slight oscillations to 92 pounds in 1837, and to zero in 1838. Between 1839 and 1845, it never, except in one instance, exceeded 22 pounds, being for the most part much under this. The exceptional year referred to was that in which he and Sir Charles Lyell were engaged by the Government to write a report on the Haswell Colliery explosion, and then his business income rose to 112 pounds. From the end of 1845 to the day of his death, Faraday's annual professional business income was exactly zero. Taking the duration of his life into account, this son of a blacksmith, and apprentice to a bookbinder, had to decide between a fortune of 150,000 pounds on the one side, and his undowered science on the other. He chose the latter, and died a poor man. But his was the glory of holding aloft among the nations the scientific name of England for a period of forty years.

The outward and visible signs of fame were also of less account to him than to most men. He had been loaded with scientific honors from all parts of the world. Without, I imagine, a dissentient voice, he was regarded as the prince of the physical investigators of the present age. The highest scientific position in this country he had, however, never filled. When the late excellent and lamented Lord Wrottesley resigned the presidency of the Royal Society, a deputation from the council, consisting of his Lordship, Mr. Grove, and Mr. Gassiot, waited upon Faraday, to urge him to accept the president's chair. All that argument or friendly persuasion could do was done to induce him to yield to the wishes of the council, which was also the unanimous wish of scientific men. A knowledge of the quickness of his own nature had induced in Faraday the habit of requiring an interval of reflection, before he decided upon any question of importance. In the present instance he followed his usual habit, and begged for a little time.

On the following morning, I went up to his

room and said on entering that I had come to him with some anxiety of mind. He demanded its cause, and I responded: "Lest you should have decided against the wishes of the deputation that waited on you yesterday." "You would not urge me to undertake this responsibility," he said. "I not only urge you," was my reply, "but I consider it your bounden duty to accept it." He spoke of the labor that it would involve; urged that it was not in his nature to take things easy; and that if he became president, he would surely have to stir many new questions, and agitate for some changes. I said that in such cases he would find himself supported by the youth and strength of the Royal Society. This, however, did not seem to satisfy him. Mrs. Faraday came into the room, and he appealed to her. Her decision was adverse, and I deprecated her decision. "Tyndall," he said at length, "I must remain plain Michael Faraday to the last. And let me now tell you, that if I accepted the honor which the Royal Society desires to confer upon me, I would not answer for the integrity of my intellect for a single year." I urged him no more, and Lord Wrottesley had a most worthy successor in Sir Benjamin Brodie.

After the death of the Duke of Northumberland, our Board of Managers wished to see Mr.

Faraday finish his career as President of the Institution, which he had entered on weekly wages more than half a century before. But he would have nothing to do with the presidency. He wished for rest, and the reverent affection of his friends was to him infinitely more precious than all the honors of official life.

The first requisite of the intellectual life of Faraday was the independence of his mind; and, though prompt to urge obedience where obedience was due, with every right assertion of manhood he intensely sympathized. Even rashness on the side of honor found him ready forgiveness, if not open applause. The wisdom of years, tempered by a character of this kind, rendered his counsel peculiarly precious to men sensitive like himself. I often sought that counsel, and, with your permission, will illustrate its character by one or two typical instances.

In 1855, I was appointed examiner under the Council for Military Education. At that time, as indeed now, I entertained strong convictions as to the enormous utility of physical science to officers of artillery and engineers, and whenever opportunity offered, I expressed this conviction without reserve. I did not think the recognition, though considerable, accorded to physical science in those examinations at all proportionate to its importance; and this probably rendered me more jealous than I otherwise should have been of its claims.

In Trinity College, Dublin, a school had been organized with reference to the Woolwich examinations, and a large number of exceedingly well-instructed young gentlemen were sent over from Dublin, to compete for appointments in the artillery and the engineers. The result of one examination was particularly satisfactory to me; indeed the marks obtained appeared so eloquent that I forbore saying a word about them. My colleagues, however, followed the usual custom of sending in brief reports with their returns of marks. After the results were published, a leading article appeared in *The Times,* in which the reports were largely quoted, praise being bestowed on all the candidates, except the excellent young fellows who had passed through my hands.

A letter from Trinity College drew my attention to this article, bitterly complaining that whereas the marks proved them to be the best of all, the science candidates were wholly ignored. I tried to set matters right by publishing on my own responsibility, a letter in *The Times*. The act, I knew, could not bear justification from the War

Office point of view; and I expected and risked the displeasure of my superiors. The merited reprimand promptly came. "Highly as the Secretary of State for War might value the expression of Professor Tyndall's opinion, he begged to say that an examiner, appointed by His Royal Highness the Commander-in-Chief, had no right to appear in the public papers as Professor Tyndall has done, without the sanction of the War Office." Nothing could be more just than this reproof, but I did not like to rest under it. I wrote a reply, and previous to sending it took it up to Faraday. We sat together before his fire, and he looked very earnest as he rubbed his hands and pondered. The following conversation then passed between us:

F. You certainly have received a reprimand, Tyndall; but the matter is over, and if you wish to accept the reproof, you will hear no more about it.

T. But I do not wish to accept it.

F. Then you know what the consequence of sending that letter will be?

T. I do.

F. They will dismiss you.

T. I know it.

F. *Then send the letter!*

The letter was firm, but respectful; it acknowledged the justice of the censure, but expressed neither repentance nor regret. Faraday, in his gracious way, slightly altered a sentence or two to make it more respectful still. It was duly sent, and on the following day I entered the Institution with the conviction that my dismissal was there before me. Weeks, however, passed. At length the well-known envelope appeared, and I broke the seal, not doubting the contents. They were very different from what I expected. "The Secretary of State for War has received Professor Tyndall's letter, and *deems the explanation therein given perfectly satisfactory.*" I have often wished for an opportunity of publicly acknowledging this liberal treatment, proving, as it did, that Lord Panmure could discern and make allowance for a good intention, though it involved an offense against routine. For many years subsequently it was my privilege to act under that excellent body, the Council for Military Education.

On another occasion of this kind, having encouraged me in a somewhat hardy resolution I had formed, Faraday backed his encouragement by an illustration drawn from his own life. The subject will interest you, and it is so sure to be talked about in the world, that no avoidable harm can rise from its introduction here.

In the year 1835, Sir Robert Peel wished to offer Faraday a pension, but that great statesman quitted office before he was able to realize his wish. The Minister who founded these pensions intended them, I believe, to be marks of honor which even proud men might accept without compromise of independence. When, however, the intimation first reached Faraday in an unofficial way, he wrote a letter announcing his determination to decline the pension; and stating that he was quite competent to earn his livelihood himself. That letter still exists, but it was never sent, Faraday's repugnance having been overruled by his friends. When Lord Melbourne came into office, he desired to see Faraday; and probably in utter ignorance of the man—for unhappily for them and us, Ministers of State in England are only too often ignorant of great Englishmen—his Lordship said something that must have deeply displeased his visitor. All the circumstances were once communicated to me, but I have forgotten the details. The term "humbug," I think, was incautiously employed by his Lordship, and other expressions were used of a similar kind. Faraday quitted the Minister with his own resolves, and that evening he left his card and a short and decisive note at the residence of Lord Melbourne.

stating that he had manifestly mistaken his Lordship's intention of honoring science in his person,
and declining to have anything whatever to do
with the proposed pension. The good-humored
nobleman at first considered the matter a capital
joke; but he was afterwards led to look at it more
seriously. An excellent lady, who was a friend both
to Faraday and the Minister, tried to arrange matters between them; but she found Faraday very
difficult to move from the position he had assumed. After many fruitless efforts, she at length
begged of him to state what he would require of
Lord Melbourne to induce him to change his mind.
He replied, "I should require from his Lordship
what I have no right or reason to expect that he
would grant—a written apology for the words he
permitted himself to use to me." The required
apology came, frank and full, creditable, I
thought, alike to the Prime Minister and the philosopher.

Considering the enormous strain imposed on
Faraday's intellect, the boylike buoyancy even of
his later years was astonishing. He was often pros-
trate, but he had immense resiliency, which he
brought into action by getting away from London
whenever his health failed. I have already indicated
the thoughts which filled his mind during the eve-

ning of his life. He brooded on magnetic media and lines of force; and the great object of the last investigation he ever undertook was the decision of the question whether magnetic force requires *time* for its propagation. How he proposed to attack this subject we may never know. But he has left some beautiful apparatus behind: delicate wheels and pinions, and associated mirrors, which were to have been employed in the investigation. The mere conception of such an inquiry is an illustration of his strength and hopefulness, and it is impossible to say to what results it might have led him. But the work was too heavy for his tired brain. It was long before he could bring himself to relinquish it and during this struggle he often suffered from fatigue of mind. It was at this period, and before he resigned himself to the repose which marked the last two years of his life, that he wrote to me the following letter—one of many priceless letters now before me—which reveals, more than anything another pen could express, the state of his mind at the time. I was sometimes censured in his presence for my doings in the Alps, but his constant reply was, "Let him alone, he knows how to take care of himself." In this letter, anxiety on this score reveals itself for the first time.

Hampton Court, August 1, 1864.

My Dear Tyndall—I do not know whether my letter will catch you, but I will risk it, though feeling very unfit to communicate with a man whose life is as vivid and active as yours; but the receipt of your kind letter makes me to know that, though I forget, I am not forgotten, and though I am not able to remember at the end of a line what was said at the beginning of it, the imperfect marks will convey to you some sense of what I long to say. We had heard of your illness through Miss Moore, and I was therefore very glad to learn that you are now quite well; do not run too many risks or make your happiness depend too much upon dangers, or the hunting of them. Sometimes the very thinking of you, and what you may be about, wearies *me* with fears, and then the cogitations pause and change, but without giving me rest. I know that much of this depends upon my own worn-out nature, and I do not know why I write it, save that when I write to you I cannot help thinking it, and the thoughts stand in the way of other matter.

*   *   *   *   *

See what a strange desultory epistle I am writing to you, and yet I feel so weary that I long to leave my desk and go to the couch.

My dear wife and Jane desire their kindest remembrances; I hear them in the next room; . . . I forget —but not you, my dear Tyndall, for I am

Ever yours,

M. FARADAY

This weariness subsided when he relinquished his work, and I have a cheerful letter from him, written in the autumn of 1865. But towards the close of that year he had an attack of illness, from which he never completely rallied. He continued to attend the Friday Evening Meetings, but the advance of infirmity was apparent to us all. Complete rest became finally essential to him, and he ceased to appear among us. There was no pain in his decline to trouble the memory of those who loved him. Slowly and peacefully he sank towards his final rest, and when it came, his death was a falling asleep. In the fulness of his honors and of his age he quitted us; the good fight fought, the work of duty—shall I not say of glory?—done. The "Jane" referred to in the foregoing letter is Faraday's niece, Miss Jane Barnard, who with an affection raised almost to religious devotion watched and tended him to the end.

I saw Mr. Faraday for the first time on my return from Marburg in 1850. I came to the Royal Institution, and sent up my card, with a copy of the paper which Knoblauch and myself had just completed. He came down and conversed with me for half an hour. I could not fail to remark the wonderful play of intellect and kindly feeling exhibited by his countenance. When he was in good

health the question of his age would never occur
to you. In the light and laughter of his eyes you
never thought of his grey hairs. He was then on
the point of publishing one of his papers on
magnecrystallic action, and he had time to refer
in a flattering note to the memoir I placed in his
hands. I returned to Germany, worked there for
nearly another year, and in June, 1851, came back
finally from Berlin to England. Then, for the first
time, and on my way to the meeting of the British
Association, at Ipswich, I met a man who has since
made his mark upon the intellect of his time; who
has long been, and who by the strong law of natural affinity must continue to be, a brother to me.
We were both without definite outlook at the
time, needing proper work, and only anxious to
have it to perform. The chairs of Natural History
and of Physics being advertised as vacant in the
University of Toronto, we applied for them, he
for the one, I for the other; but, possibly guided
by a prophetic instinct, the University authorities
declined having anything to do with either of us.
If I remember aright, we were equally unlucky
elsewhere.

One of Faraday's earliest letters to me had reference to this Toronto business, which he thought
it unwise in me to neglect. But Toronto had its

own notions, and in 1853, at the instance of Dr. Bence Jones, and on the recommendation of Faraday himself, a chair of physics at the Royal Institution was offered to me. I was tempted at the same time to go elsewhere, but a strong attraction drew me to his side. Let me say that it was mainly his and other friendships, precious to me beyond all expression, that caused me to value my position here more highly than any other that could be offered to me in this land. Nor is it for its honor, though surely that is great, but for the strong personal ties that bind me to it, that I now chiefly prize this place. You might not credit me were I to tell you how lightly I value the honor of being Faraday's successor compared with the honor of having been Faraday's friend. His friendship was energy and inspiration; his "mantle" is a burden almost too heavy to be borne.

Sometimes during the last year of his life, by the permission or invitation of Mrs. Faraday, I went up to his rooms to see him. The deep radiance, which in his time of strength flashed with such extraordinary power from his countenance, had subsided to a calm and kindly light, by which my latest memory of him is warmed and illuminated. I knelt one day beside him on the carpet and placed my hand upon his knee; he stroked it affectionately, smiled, and murmured, in a low soft voice, the last words that I remember as having been spoken to me by Michael Faraday.

It was my wish and aspiration to play the part of Schiller to this Goethe; and he was at times so strong and joyful—his body so active, and his intellect so clear—as to suggest to me the thought that he, like Goethe, would see the younger man laid low. Destiny ruled otherwise, and now he is but a memory to us all. Surely no memory could be more beautiful. He was equally rich in mind and heart. The fairest traits of a character sketched by Paul found in him perfect illustration. For he was "blameless, vigilant, sober, of good behavior, apt to teach, not given to filthy lucre." He had not a trace of worldly ambition; he declared his duty to his Sovereign by going to the levee once a year, but beyond this he never sought contact with the great. The life of his spirit and of his intellect was so full, that the things which men most strive after were absolutely indifferent to him. "Give me health and a day," says the brave Emerson, "and I will make the pomp of emperors ridiculous." In an eminent degree Faraday could say the same. What to him was the splendor of a palace compared with a thunderstorm upon Brighton Downs? What among all the appliances of royalty to compare with the setting sun? I refer to a thunderstorm and a sunset, because these things excited a kind of ecstasy in his mind, and to a mind open to such ecstasy the pomps and pleasures of the world are usually of small account. Nature, not education, rendered Faraday strong and refined. A favorite experiment of his own was representative of himself. He loved to show that water in crystallizing excluded all foreign ingredients, however intimately they might be mixed with it. Out of acids, alkalis, or saline solutions, the crystal came sweet and pure. By some such natural process in the formation of this man, beauty and nobleness coalesced, to the exclusion of everything vulgar and low. He did not learn his gentleness in the world, for he withdrew himself from its culture; and still this land of England contained no truer gentleman than he. Not half his greatness was incorporate in his science, for science could not reveal the bravery and delicacy of his heart.

But it is time that I should end these weak words, and lay my poor garland on the grave of this

Just and faithful knight of God.

NOTES AND APPENDIX

by Keith Gordon Irwin

NOTES

(1) *Benzol.* A colorless liquid obtained by the distillation of coal tar; now known chemically as benzene, C_6H_6.

(2) Proverbs 16:32.

(3) *The electricity of the machine, the pile, the gymnotus and torpedo.* The first is the hand-operated electric machine used as a source of frictional electricity. The second, referred to quite fully on page 73, is an invention of Volta of Italy which was the forerunner of his electric battery. In it the electric charge was produced by chemical action. The other two are fish that are capable of giving severe electrical shocks; the gymnotus is also known as the electric eel, the torpedo as the electric ray.

(4) *Bibulous paper.* A soft paper that readily "imbibes" or soaks up liquid.

(5) *Sulphurets.* An earlier name for sulphides.

(6) Faraday had used the name *ions* for electrically charged particles in solution but had not been able to explain their formation. A satisfactory theory was, in time, to be developed by the Swedish physicist Svante Arrhenius, but this came after the year 1868, when Tyndall's report was written.

(7) This statement reflects an old confusion of terms that was finally cleared up about 1870. The equivalent weight of an element was its weight that combined with or displaced a unit weight of hydrogen. This would be found by experiment; for oxygen it was 8. If the formula for water is considered to be HO, then the equivalent weight and the atomic weight agree. With the formula given as H_2O, the equivalent weight was half the atomic weight.

(8) The reference is to the two theories as to the nature of light and the matter by which light reaches a new position. The first was that of Isaac Newton of England in which he supposed that light consists of elastic particles of inconceivable minuteness shot out by luminous bodies. The second theory was that of Thomas Young of England in which he supposed that light was a wave motion set in action by a luminous body.

(9) *Contiguous particles.* Particles neighboring and almost touching.

(10) The reference is to the discussion of the optical glass as given on pages 18–19.

(11) *Silbergroschen.* The name, in German, of a small silver coin.

(12) Faraday, whose science was self-taught, had no knowledge of advanced mathematics and was not "versed in mechanics." (See page 87, lines 13–16.)

APPENDIX

This book, which reports on the great experimental work of Michael Faraday, particularly in electricity, was written for the people of 1868. At that time, Thomas A. Edison and Alexander Graham Bell were twenty-one. For such young men, and others like them, the experiments were tremendously exciting. Faraday's work was the "springboard" for the great inventive advance in America that would spread the use of electricity across the continent.

The book does not, however, mention electrons, refer to the structure of atoms, or consider the charges upon ions. These ideas were to come later—much later. The reader, then, who seeks to understand the experimental results *in terms of modern theory* must do that for himself.

There are many points that will interest the general reader as being thought-provoking in their nature. I have picked out a few:

Faraday's estimate of the amount of electrical force as lightning needed to decompose one grain-weight of water. Page 53, line 14, to page 54, line 3.

His argument about electricity and perpetual motion. Page 76, line 18, to page 79, line 10.

His comments on the future of the study of molecular forces (today represented by the growth of physical chemistry). Page 121, lines 7 to 26.

His suggestion that the magnetic nature of oxygen in the atmosphere *may* be responsible for variations in the earth's magnetism. Page 140, line 3, to page 143, line 9.

His speculations on the force that we call gravity. Page 150, line 11, to page 152, line 2.

His speculations on magnetic lines of force. Page 152, line 3, to page 155, line 10.

Tyndall's comments, given at length, on the unity and convertibility of natural forces. Page 160, line 1, to page 171, line 9.

INDEX

JOHN TYNDALL was a nineteenth-century British physicist, who is remembered today more for clarifying obscure contributions made by other scientists than for his own research. He was chosen professor of natural philosophy at the Royal Institution in 1854. There he met Michael Faraday, and the two became close friends. *Faraday as a Discoverer,* published one year after Faraday's death in 1867, is a group of lectures which Tyndall compiled in memory of his friend.

Tyndall was born in 1820 in County Carlow, Ireland. A "self-made man," he was first stimulated to study by the historical essays of Thomas Carlyle. By intense dedication to his work, he prepared himself for the University of Marburg in 1848 and received his doctoral degree two years later. Among his scientific investigations, Tyndall is most noted for his work with the transparency and opacity of gases and vapors for radiant heat. He died in 1893.

KEITH GORDON IRWIN has devoted almost half a century of his life to teaching. He became professor of chemistry and physics at Penn College in Iowa when he was twenty-one. Since then, he has taught these subjects in high schools, colleges, and universities in Illinois, Missouri, Kansas, and Colorado. In 1955 Mr. Irwin retired from the faculty staff at Colorado State University as a professor emeritus in the College of Science and Arts.

Writing and illustrating books was originally a hobby for him, but he has become increasingly concerned with this aspect of education since his successful publication of three books, introductions to science classics, and numerous magazine articles.

Mr. Irwin was born on a farm near Galesburg, Illinois, and has moved frequently to accommodate his teaching. He and his family went to Colorado in 1923 and are now living in Fort Collins.